6.⁰⁰

9.

ANANGA RANGA

THE HINDU ART OF LOVE

ANANGA RANGA

STAGE OF THE BODILESS ONE

THE HINDU ART OF LOVE

by

KALAYANA MALLA

TRANSLATED AND ANNOTATED

by

F. F. ARBUTHNOT and

RICHARD F. BURTON

and

PHARMACOPEIA "ARS AMORIS INDICA"

by

H. S. GABERS

and S. RAMA

MEDICAL PRESS OF NEW YORK

1964

NEW YORK, 1964
MEDICAL PRESS OF NEW YORK

CONTENTS.

		Page.
The Dedication	. . . .	iii.
The Preface	. . . .	vii.
The Introduction	. . . .	

CHAPTER I.

| Of the Four Orders of Women | . . . . | 1 |

CHAPTER II.

| Of the Various sorts of Passion in Women | . . | 8 |

CHAPTER III.

| Of the Different kinds of Men and Women | . . | 15 |

CHAPTER IV.

| Description of the General Qualities, Characteristics, Temperaments of Women | . . . . . | 24 |

CHAPTER V.

| Characteristics of Women of Various Lands | . . | 33 |

CHAPTER VI.

| On Useful Medicines | . . . . . . | 38 |

CHAPTER VII.

| Treating of Vashikaran, or the Art of Fascination by use of Charms | . . . . | 69 |

CHAPTER VIII.

Page.

Of different Signs in Men and Women . . . 77

CHAPTER IX.

Treating of External Enjoyments 97

CHAPTER X.

Treating of Internal Enjoyments 115

Appendix I 131

Appendix II 139

PREFACE.

THE following pages contain a Hindu "Art of Love," which may fairly be pronounced unique. From the days of Sotades and Ovid to our time, western authors have treated the subject either jocularly or with a tendency to hymn the joys of immorality, and the gospel of debauchery. The Indian author has taken the opposite view, and it is impossible not to admire the delicacy with which he has handled an exceedingly delicate theme. As he assures his readers before parting, the object of the book, which opens with praises of the gods, is not to encourage chambering and wantonness, but simply and in all sincerity to prevent the separation of husband and wife. Feeling convinced that monogamy is a happier state than polygamy, he would save the married couple from the monotony and satiety which follow possession, by varying their pleasures in every conceivable way, and by supplying them with the means of being psychically pure and physically pleasant to each other. He recognizes, fully as Balzac does, the host of evils which result from conjugal infidelity; and, if he allow adultery in order to save life, he does only what was done by the most civilized of pagan nations, who had the same opinions upon the subject: witness the liberality of Socrates in lending his wife to a friend, and the generosity of Seleucus quoted in the following pages.

Nor is it a small merit to the author, that he has been able to say so much of novelty and of interest upon the congress of the sexes, a subject which has been worked since the remotest ages, which is supposed to have been exhausted long ago, and yet which no one has treated as it is treated in this treatise. The originality is everywhere mixed up, it is true, with a peculiar quaintness, resulting from the language and from the peculiarities of Hindu thought, yet it is not the less original. Nothing can be more characteristic of the Indian than this laboured and mechanical style of love; when kisses are divided into so many kinds; when there are rules for patting with the palm and the back of the hand, and regulations for the several expirations of breath. Regarded in this light, the book becomes an ethnological treasure, which tells us as much of Hindu human nature as the "Thousand Nights and a Night" of Arab manners and customs in the *cinquecento*.

The author informs us that the treatise was composed by the Arch-poet Kalyána Mall (himself), and unfortunately we know little of him. A biography of the poets, the Kavi-Charika, states that he was a native of Kalinga, by caste a Brahman, who flourished during the reign of Anangabhima, alias Ladadiva, the King of that country; and an inscription in the Sanctuary of Jagannath proves that the Rajah built a temple in the Shaka, or year of Shalivana, 1094 = A. D. 1172.

On the other hand all MSS. of the Ananga-Ranga have a verse distinctly stating that the author Kalyána Mall, wrote the book for the amusement of Lada Khan, son of Ahmed, of the Lodi House. Hence the suggestion that the patron was Ahmad Chan, Subahdár or Viceroy of Gujarat (Guzerat) whom, with Eastern flattery and exaggeration, the poet crowns King of the Realm. This Officer was a servant of the Lodi or Pathán dynasty, who according to Elphinstone appointed many of their kinsmen to high office. Three Lodi kings (Bahlúl, Sikandar and Abrahim, who ruled between A. D. 1450 and 1526) immediately preceded the Taymur house in the person of Baber Shah. The work, which is not written in classical style and belongs to late Sanskrit literature, is an analysis of and a compilation from treatises of much earlier date, such as the Kama Sutra of Vatsyáyana (for which see Chapt. vi.) the Ratiràhasya, the Panchasáyaka, the Smarapradipa, the Ratimanjari and, to quote no other, the Mánasolása or Abhilashitachintamani—the "Description of the King's Diversion," *le Roi s'amuse*.

The treatise, originally in Sanskrit, has been translated into every language of the East which boasts a literature, however humble. In Sanskrit and Prakrit (Marathi, Gujarati, Bengáli, etc.) it is called "Ananga-

Ranga," Stage or form of the Bodiless one, Káma Deva (Kamadeva), the Hindu Cupid who was reduced to ashes by the fiery eye of Shiva and presently restored to life. The legend runs thus in Moore's "Hindu Pantheon:"—

"Mahadeva, *i. e.* Shiva, and Parvati his wife, playing with dice at the game of Chaturanga, disputed and parted in wrath; and severally performing rigid acts of devotion to the Supreme Being, kindled thereby such vehement fires as threatened a general conflagration. The Devas, in great alarm, hastened to Brahma, who led them to Mahadeva and supplicated him to recall his consort; but the wrathful god answered, that she must return to him of her own free choice. They accordingly deputed Ganga, the river-goddess, who prevailed on Parvati to return to her husband, on the condition that his love for her should be restored. The celestial mediators then employed Kamadeva, who wounded Shiva with one of his flowery arrows, but the angry deity reduced the God of Love to ashes. Parvati, soon after presenting herself before Shiva in the semblance of a Kerati, or daughter of a mountaineer, and seeing him enamoured of her, assumed her own shape and effected a re-union. The relenting Shiva consoled the afflicted Rati, the widow of Kama, by assuring her that she should rejoin her husband, when she should be born again in the form of Pradyamna, son of Krishna, and put Sambará Asura to death. This favourable prediction was in due time accomplished, and Pradyamna was seized by the demon Sambara, who placed him in a chest and threw it into the sea. The chest was swallowed by a large fish, which was caught and carried to the palace of the giant, where the unfortunate Rati had been compelled to perform manual service; it fell to her lot to open the fish, and finding the chest and its contents, she nursed the infant in private, and educated him until he had sufficient strength to destroy the malignant Sambara. He had before considered Rati as his mother; but their minds being now irradiated, the prophetic promise of Mahadeva was remembered, and the god of Love was re-united to the goddess of Pleasure."

In Arabic, Hindostani and the Moslem dialects, the Ananga-Ranga becomes Lizzat al-Nisá, or the Pleasures of Women; and it appears with little change in Persian and Turkish. Generally it is known in India as the Kamá Shástra, the Scripture of Káma or Lila Shástra, the Scripture of Play or amorous Sport— τὸ παίζειν. The vulgar call it "Koka Pandit," from the supposed author, concerning whom the following tale is told. A woman who was burning with love and could find none to satisfy her inordinate desires, threw off her clothes and swore she would wander the world naked till she met with her match. In this condition she entered the levee-hall of the Rajah upon whom Koka Pandit was attending; and, when asked if she were not ashamed of herself, looked insolently at the crowd of courtiers around her and scornfully declared that there was not a man in the room. The King and his company were sore abashed; but the Sage joining his hands, applied with due humility for royal permission to tame the shrew. He then led her home and worked so persuasively that wellnigh fainting from fatigue and from repeated orgasms she cried for quarter. Thereupon the virile Pandit inserted gold pins into her arms and legs; and, leading her before his Rajah, made her confess her defeat and solemnly veil herself in the presence. The Rajah was, as might be expected, anxious to learn how the victory had been won, and commanded Koka Pandit to tell his tale, and to add much useful knowledge on the subject of coition. In popular pictures the Sage appears sitting before and lecturing the Rajah who duly throned and shaded by the Chatri, or royal canopy, with his harem fanning him and forming tail, lends an attentive ear to the words of wisdom.

In these days the Ananga-Ranga enjoys deserved celebrity. Lithographed copies have been printed by hundreds of thousands, and the book is in the hands of both sexes and all ages throughout the nearer East, and possibly it may extend to China and Japan. It has become a part of natural life, and even the "Fables of Pilpay," to use a neutral term for a volume whose names are manifold, has not a wider circulation.

The Kama Sutra of Vatsyáyana, concerning which more presently, and Ananga-Ranga must be regarded as two valuable and interesting works on Social Science: they bear repeated readings and seem ever to present a something of novelty. Eastern students often apply to them the well-known lines of Hafiz:—

> Oh songster sweet, begin the lay,
> Ever fresh and ever gay;
> For us once more the tale renew,
> Ever old but ever new.

It was at first our intention, after rendering the "Káma Shastra" from Sanskrit into English, to dress it up in Latin, that it might not fall into the hands of the vulgar. But further considerations satisfied us that it contains nothing essentially immoral, and much matter deserving of more consideration than it receives at present. The generation which prints and reads literal English translations of the debauched Petronius Arbiter, and the witty indecencies of Rabelais, can hardly be prudish enough to complain of the devout and highly moral Kalyána Malla. At least, so think

THE TRANSLATORS.

INDIAN SCULPTURE

In India the union of male and female has become the symbol, from the earliest times for the union of all cosmic forces and the pleasure of the body in mating became, under accepted religious doctrines and social forms, linked with the sanctity of procreation and an end in itself. The concept of the original sin and sexual secretiveness never formed any part of the intense phases of Indian culture.

Thus it was that in Indian plastic art, the human form became the expression of the sculptor's vision of the life force. The abstract and mystic values of religion were always realized in the concrete imagery of the human body, exaggerated and dramatized to the supernatural proportions of gods and goddesses, instinct with the sap of life.

In such an atmosphere, it is not surprising that the Maithuna (loving) couples abound, from earliest cave temples through the mediaeval period down till the 18th century, as the very consecration of the drama of sex, energy flowing in myriad forms. And they are carved without any prurience but with the utmost tenderness and sensuous beauty.

. . . in Khajoraho there becomes visible, within the precincts of a group of temples, creative architecture and sculpture enough to compare with the products of the whole European Renaissance, the awe-struck visitor is merely dumb and aghast in the vain attempt to understand how such miraculous achievement were at all possible . . .

. . . For to go to Khajuraho, Bhuvaneshwar, Konavak or Puri involves an act of surrender to the accent of other ages . . . and the acceptance of the primary truth stated by the dramatic critic Dhananjaya that "those who lack imagination are no better than furniture, walls or stones."

. . . One should walk around the pillars in reverence at the sheer grandeur of execution of concepts seldom rendered in stone with such devotion, resulting in beauties which are commensurate with the greatest of world art. And, then, if one's eyes are filled with the bewildering multiplicity of forms there may come the promise of a spiritual insight to the dreams of those who stood poised

between the shining surface of reality and the inner core of spiritual radiance.

Mulk Raj Anand

In nearly all Indian art there runs a vein of deep sex-mysticism. Not only are female forms felt to be equal appropriate with male to adumbrate the majesty of the Over-Soul, but the interplay of all psychic and physical sexual forces is felt in itself to be religious.

Here is no thought that passion is degrading — as some Christian and Buddhists monks and many moderns have regarded it, but a frank recognition of the close analogy between amorous and religious ecstasy. How rich and varied must have been the emotional experience of a society to which life could appear so perfectly transparent, and where at the same time the most austere asceticism was a beloved ideal for all those who sought to pass over life's Wandering! It is thus that the artist, speaking always for the people, rather than of personal idiosyncrasies, set side by side on his cathedral walls the yogi and apsara, the saint and courtesan; accepting life as he saw it, he interpreted all its phenomena with perfect catholicity of vision.

The Indian sex-symbolism assure two main forms, the recognition of which will assist the student of arts first, the desire and union of men and women, sacramental in its likeness to the union of the soul with God — this is

XVII

the love of herd-girls for Krishna; and second, the creation of the world, manifestations, lila, as the fruit of the union of male and female cosmic principles — purusha and shakti.

The beautiful erotic art of Konarak clearly signifies the quickening power of the Sun, perhaps not without an element of sympathetic magic . . . They appear in Indian Temple sculpture simply because voluptuous ecstasy has also its due place in life: and those who interpreted life were artists. To them such figures appeared appropriate equally for happiness they represented and for their deeper symbolism.

*Coomaraswamy
in Arts and Crafts of India and Ceylon*

In the matter of sexual relationship Indian civilization, in every stratum of society, holds up a standard of morality as high as Europe has ever done.

The idea connected with sex symbolism in Hindu art and ritual are generally misinterpreted by those who take them out of the environment of Indian social life. In the Upanishads the sexual relationship is described as one of the means of apprehending the divine nature, and throughout Oriental literature it is constantly used metaphorically to express the true relationship between the human soul and God.

*E. B. Havell
in Ideals of Indian Art*

XVIII

In all archaic religions occasional promiscuity formed part of public worship. The phenomenon of reproduction and the precedent sex activity led the ancients to believe in the efficacy of promiscuity as a fertilizing agent of their fields. Spring and autumn, the seasons during which the verdant earth puts on a vestment of gaiety and the animal and vegetable kingdoms are at their best, were particularly selected for celebration of festivals connected with the principles of regeneration. In ancient Babylon, Egypt and Greece there were temples dedicated to gods and goddesses of reproduction, and during the spring festivals in these temples the ordinary morality of the society was given up in favour of licentious behaviour for the pleasure of the deities. Hinduism is coeval with the religions of Babylon, Egypt and Greece though it has survived them. Many of the goddesses of the Babylonian, Egyptian and Greek pantheon may still be found in Hinduism though known under different names.

The ruins of the temples of North India show that the practice of sex cults were prevalent in many of them. In almost all the great temples that have survived the ravages of middle ages the decorative art consists of erotic sculptures. Some of these show coital postures illustrative of Vatsyayana's treatise on the subject. The great temple of Konarak, now in ruins, was particularly noted for its erotic sculptures. The temple was dedicated to Surya the sun god. Sun temples are now few in India, but at one time his worship was fairly widespread; and a

XIX

characteristic feature of the architecture of temples dedicated to the sun god is the erotic sculptures that form part of the decorative art.

It is not, however, the sun god alone who delights in erotic art. The famous temple of Jagannath in Orissa, the Khajuraho temples, and most of the imposing shrines of South India have erotic carving as forming part of decorative art. Apart from the fascination the mystic has always had for sex, the Hindu sculptor seems to have found in Maithuna (sexual union) an interesting motif. It is a peculiarity of the erotic sculptures of the temples that they appear mainly on the outer shrines and not on the inner. This circumstance has led some writers to believe that the idea emphasized is that the worshipper should be able to give free vent to his imagination outside the shrine and cast away all lascivious thoughts before entering it. This is a modern interpretation inspired by the Western notion of the indecency of sex, and it is doubtful if this was the real intention of the builders of the temple. The Hindus, do not consider sex as something outside the province of religion, but on the contrary emphasize the importance of sex force in all their religious conceptions. As such its universality and greatness are probably indicated to the worshipper by means of art.

P. Thomas
in Kama Kalpa

XX

The art of India illustrates frequently scenes of love: divine loves — union of cosmic principles symbolized by the sexual union of Mithovna. These amorous representations, dating from the 9th century, are multiplied marking the resurgence of the old pre-aryan cults. Thus the middle-age liberates Hindu thought from Brahman control.

We have chosen the admirable reliefs of ancient temples (X - XII century) of which we present here a practically hitherto unpublished collection — to illustrate Ananga-Ranga, because they, the admirable reliefs, represent in the domain of sculpture as the work of Jayadeva in that of poetry, the highest of art and thought of Hindu Middle-Age.

Shri Jayadeva

INTRODUCTION.

MAY you be purified by Parvati[1] who coloured the nails of her hands which were white like the waters of Ganges, with lac after seeing the fire on the forehead of Shambu; who painted her eyes with collyrium after seeing the dark hues of Shambhu's neck and whose body-hair stood erect (with desire) after seeing in a mirror the ashes on Shambhu's body.

I invoke thee, O Kámadeva! thee the sportive; thee, the wanton one, who dwellest in the hearts of all created beings;

Thou instillest courage in time of war; thou destroyedst Sambar' A'sura and the Rákshasas; thou sufficest unto Rati,[2] and to the loves and pleasures of the world;

Thou art ever cheerful, removing uneasiness and

[1] The mountain-goddess of many names, wife of Shiva, the third person of the Hindu Trinity, who is here termed Shambhu for Swayambhu, the Self-Existent. The invocation is abrupt and does not begin with the beginning, Ganesha (Janus), Lord of Incepts, who is invariably invoked by the Hindu, that he may further the new undertaking. This god is worshipped under the form of a short stout man, with an elephant's trunk and protuberant belly. (See Vol. III. p. 38, "A View of the History, Literature, and Mythology of the Hindus," by William Ward, of Serampore, London, 1832.) The loves of Krishna and the sixteen thousand milkmaids are recorded in the Báhgavat: this eleventh incarnation of Vishnú is a dark-blue man, playing with both hands upon the pipe, whilst Rada, his wife, stands on his left side. Kámadeva, or the Hindu Cupid, the son of Bramhá, is represented as a beautiful youth, the most lovely of all the gods, holding a bow and flower-tipped arrow, with which, while wandering through perfumed glades, accompanied by Rati, his spouse, he wounds the hearts of the inhabitants of the Triloka or Three Worlds. Sir William Jones says that he appears to correspond with the Greek Eros and the Roman Cupido, but that the Indian description of his person and arms, his family, attendants and attributes has new and peculiar beauties. Sambar' Asura was one of the Rakshasas, gigantic and diabolical beings, whom Kama slew.

[2] The Sakti, or female principle, representing the aptitude of conception and continuation, becomes the wives of the gods in

over activity, and thou givest comfort and happiness to the mind of man.

King Ahmad was the ornament of the Lodí House. He was a Sea, having for waters the tears shed by the widows of his slaughtered foes, and he rose to just renown and wide-spread fame. May his son Láda Khan, versed in the Kama Shastra, or Scripture of Love, and having his feet rubbed with the diadems of other kings, be ever victorious!

The great princely sage and arch-poet, Kalyána Malla, versed in all the arts, after consulting many wise and holy men, and having examined the opinions of many poets, and extracted the essence of their wisdom, composed, with a view of pleasing his sovereign, a work which was called Ananga-Ranga.[1] May it ever be appreciated by the discerning, for it hath been dedicated to those who are desirous of studying the art and mystery of man's highest enjoyment, and to those who are best acquainted with the science and practice of dalliance and love-delight.

It is true that no joy in the world of mortals can compare with that derived from the knowledge of the Creator. Second, however, and subordinate only to this,

Hindu mythology. Thus in the Shavya-Purana, Shiva says, "from the supreme spirit proceed Parusha" (the generative or male principle) "and Parkriti" (the productive, or female principle), and by them was produced the universe, the manifestation of the one god." For its origin we must go back to the Chaldaeo-Babylonian System.

[1] This title has been explained: see also Ward iii. 179. Káma was the son of Maya (= Illusion, the attracting powers of Matter, Maia the mother of Mercury), he married Rati (Affection, vulgarized in our "rut") and is bosom-friend to Vasanta, Basant or Spring.

are the satisfaction and pleasure arising from the possession of a beautiful woman. Men, it is true, marry for the sake of undisturbed congress, as well as for love and comfort, and often they obtain handsome and attractive wives. But they do not give them plenary contentment, nor do they themselves thoroughly enjoy their charms. The reason of which is, that they are purely ignorant of the Scripture of Cupid, the Káma Shastra; and, despising the difference between the several kinds of women, they regard them only in an animal point of view. Such men must be looked upon as foolish and unintelligent; and this book is composed with the object of preventing lives and loves being wasted in similar manner, and the benefits to be derived from its study are set forth in the following verses:—

"The man who knoweth the Art of Love, and who understandeth the thorough and varied enjoyment of woman;

"As advancing age cooleth his passions, he learneth to think of his Creator, to study religious subjects, and to acquire divine knowledge:

"Hence he is freed from further transmigration of souls; and when the tale of his days is duly told, he goeth direct with his wife to the Svarga (heaven)."

And thus all you who read this book shall know how delicious an instrument is woman, when artfully played upon; how capable she is of producing the most exquisite harmony; of executing the most complicated variations and of giving the divinest pleasures.

Finally, let it be understood that every Shloka (stanza) of this work has a double signification, after the fashion of the Vedanta, and may be interpreted in two ways, either mystical or amatory.

ANANGA-RANGA;

OR,

THE HINDU ART OF LOVE.

CHAPTER I.

SECTION I.

Of the Four Orders of Women.

FIRST, let it be understood, that women must be divided into four classes of temperament. These are:—

1. Padminí;
2. Chitriní;
3. Shankhiní; and
4. Hastiní.

The same correspond with the four different phases of Moksha, or Release from further Transmigration. The first is Sáyujyatá, or absorption into the essence of the Deity; the second is Sámípyatá, nearness to the Deity, the being born in the Divine Presence; the third is Sarúpatá, or resemblance to the Deity in limbs and material body;

the fourth and last is Salokatá, or residence in the heaven of some especial god.

For the name of woman is Nárí, which, being interpreted, means "No A'rí," or foe; and such is Moksha, or absorption, because all love it and it loves all mankind.

Padminí, then means Sáyujyatá, also called Khadginí-Moksha (Sword-release) the absorption of man into the Náráyan (godhead), who lives in the Khshírábdí, or Milksea, one of the Seven Oceans, and from whose navel sprang the Padma, or Lotus-flower.

Chitriní is Sámípyatá-Moksha, like those who, having been incarnated as gods, perform manifold and wonderful works. Shankhiní is Sarúpatá-Moksha, even as the man who takes the form of Vishnú, bears upon his body the Shankha (conch-shell), the Chakra or discus, and other emblems of that god. The Hastiní is Salokatá-Moksha, for she is what residence in Vishnu's heaven is to those of the fourth class who have attributes and properties, shape and form, hands and feet.

SECTION II.

Personal Peculiarities of the Four Classes.

AND now learn ye by these words to distinguish from one another the four orders of woman-kind.

She in whom the following signs and symptoms appear, is called Padminí, or Lotus-woman.[1] Her face is pleasing

---

1 Evidently the nervous temperament, with due admixture of the bilious and sanguine.

as the full moon ; her body, well clothed with flesh, is soft as the Shiras[1] or mustard-flower ; her skin is fine, tender and fair as the yellow lotus, never dark-coloured, though resembling, in the effervescence and purple light of her youth, the cloud about to burst. Her eyes are bright and beautiful as the orbs of the fawn, well-cut, and with reddish corners. Her bosom is hard, full and high ; her neck is goodly shaped as the conch-shell, so delicate that the saliva can be seen through it ; her nose is straight and lovely, and three folds or wrinkles cross her middle, about the umbilical region. Her Yoni[2] resembles the opening lotus-bud, and her Love-seed (Káma-salila, the water of life)[3] is perfumed like the lily which has newly burst. She walks with swan-like gait, and her voice is low and musical as the note of the Kokila-bird[4] ; she delights in white raiment, in fine jewels, and in rich dresses. She eats little, sleeps lighly and, being as respectable and religious as she is clever and courteous, she is ever anxious to worship the gods, and to enjoy the conversation of Brahmans. Such, then, is the Padminí, or Lotus-woman.

The Chitriní, or Art-woman,[5] is of middle size, neither

[1] A lofty tree with soft and fragrant pollen.

[2] The Yoni is the feminine opposed to the Linga (Priapus) or male apparatus.

[3] See note, chap. iv., on the Hindu ideas of human sperm, and for the vermicules of the Yoni, chap. iii, sec. 3.

[4] Usually known as the Indian cuckoo, though its voice is harsh and disagreeable; in poetry and romance it takes the place of the bulbul of Persia, and the nightingale of Europe.

[5] The sanguine temperament.

short nor tall, with bee-black hair, thin, round, shell-like neck; tender body; waist lean-girthed as the lion's; hard, full breasts; well-turned thighs and heavily made hips. The hair is thin about the Yoni, the Mons Veneris being soft, raised and round. The Káma-salila (love-seed) is hot, and has the perfume of honey, producing from its abundance a sound during the venereal rite. Her eyes roll, and her walk is coquettish, like the swing of an elephant, whilst her voice is that of the peacock.[1] She is fond of pleasure and variety; she delights in singing and in every kind of accomplishment, especially the arts manual; her carnal desires are not strong, and she loves her "pets," parrots, Mainas and other birds. Such is the Chitriní, or Art-woman.

The Shankhiní,[2] or Conch-woman, is of bilious temperament, her skin being always hot and tawny, or dark yellow-brown; her body is large, her waist thick, and her breasts small; her head, hands, and feet are thin and long, and she looks out of the corners of her eyes. Her Yoni is ever moist with Káma-salila, which is distinctly salt, and the cleft is covered with thick hair. Her voice is hoarse and harsh, of the bass or contralto type; her gait is precipitate; she eats with moderation and she delights in clothes, flowers and ornaments of red colour. She is subject to fits of amorous passion, which makes her head hot and her brain confused, and at the moment of enjoy-

[1] Meaning excellent as that of the Peacock, which is not disliked by the Hindus as by Europeans. They associate it with the breaking of rainy monsoon, which brings joy to the thirsty earth and sun-parched men.

[2] The bilious temperament.

ment, she thrusts her nails into her husband's flesh.[1] She is of choleric constitution, hard-hearted, insolent and vicious; irascible, rude and ever addicted to finding fault. Such is the Shankhiní, or Conch-woman.

The Hastiní is short of stature; she has a stout, coarse body, and her skin, if fair, is of dead white: her hair is tawny, her lips are large; her voice is harsh, choked, and throaty (*voix de gorge*) and her neck is bent. Her gait is slow, and she walks in a slouching manner: often the toes of one foot are crooked. Her Káma-salila has the savour of the juice which flows in spring from the elephant's temples. She is tardy in the art of Love, and can be satisfied only by prolonged congress, in fact, the longer the better, but it will never suffice her. She is gluttonous, shameless, and irascible. Such is the Hastiní, or elephant-woman.[2]

Section III.

The days of greatest enjoyment for the Four Classes.

HAVING thus laid down the four classes of woman-kind, Kalyana Malla, the arch-poet, proceeds to give a table of

1 So Apollonius of Rhodes, describing the passions of Medeia says:—"The fire which devours her, attacks all her nerves, and makes itself felt even behind the head in that spot where pain is most poignant when an extreme fervour seizes on all the senses."

2 "Elephant"-woman, because the animal being called the "handed one," from the use of the trunk, and Hastini corresponds with Karami, from kara, a hand. She is "mulier nigris dignissima barris," and of the lymphatic or lowest temperament. These divisions represent, we have noted, roughly and unscientifically, the four European temperaments, nervous, sanguine, bilious and lymphatic. In a future chapter, the three Hindu temperaments will be discussed.

the times in which each order derives the greatest amount of pleasure from the venereal rite. These periods must be learnt by heart, and students will remember that on the other days not specified, no amount of congress will satisfy passions. Read, then, and master the elements.

TABLE.[1]

Pratipadá 1st day	Dvitiyá 2nd day	Chaturthí 4th day	Panchamí 5th day	Satisfy the Padminí
Shashatí 6th day	Ashtamí 8th day	Dashamí 10th day	Dwadashí 12th day	Satisfy the Chatriní
Tritiyá 3rd day	Saptamí 7th day	Ekádashí 11th day	Trayodasí 13th day	Satisfy the Shankhiní
Navamí 9th day	Chaturdashí 14th day	Purnima Full Moon	Amávásyá New Moon	Satisfy the Hastiní

SECTION IV.

Of the hours which give the highest enjoyment.

WOMEN, be it observed, differ greatly in the seasons which they prefer for enjoyment, according to their classes and temperaments. The Padminí, for instance, takes no satisfaction in night congress; indeed, she is thoroughly averse to it. Like the Súrya Camala (day lotus) which opens its eyes to the sun light, so she is satisfied even by a boy-husband in the bright hours. The

1 The days (Tithi) are those of the lunar fortnight: the Pratipadá, for instance, being the first, when the moon's increase and wane begin.

Chitriní and the Shankhiní are like the Chandra Kamala, or night-lotus, that expands to the rays of the moon; and the Hastiní, who is the coarsest, ignores all these delicate distinctions.

TABLE I.
Regulating the Night Hours.

1st Pahar 9 p. m.	2nd Pahar 9—12 p. m.	3rd Pahar 12—3 a. m.	4th Pahar 3—6 a. m.
"	"	"	The Padminí
The Chitriní	"	"	"
"	"	The Shankhiní	"
The Hastiní	The Hastiní	The Hastiní	The Hastiní

TABLE II.
Regulating the Day Hours.

1st Pahar 6—9 a. m.	2nd Pahar 9—12 a. m.	3rd Pahar 12—3 p. m.	4th Pahar 3—6 p. m.
The Padminí	The Padminí	The Padminí	The Padminí
"	The Hastiní	The Hastiní	"

1 As amongst the classics, day and night are divided by the Hindus with eight watches each of seven ghari, or hours (1 ghari=24l.)

The above tables, then, show the Pahar,[1] or watch of the night and day, during which the four classes of women derive the greatest pleasure.

And here it will be observed that the Chitriní and the Shankhiní derive no satisfaction from day-congress.

Thus did the arch-poet, Kalyana Malla, relate unto Ladkhan Rajah how women are divided into four classes, each of which has its own peculiarity of body and mind, and its several times of enjoyments, according to ʿ' state of the moon and the hour of the day or nigʿ

CHAPTER II.

Of the various seats of Passion in Women.

AND, further, let men know that passion resides in different parts and members of the woman's person, and that by applying to these the necessary Chandrakalá,[1] or preparatory *attouchements,* great comfort and pleasure are experienced by both husband and wife. On the other hand, if the process placed in the table opposite the respective days of the lunar fortnight be not performed, neither sex will be thoroughly satisfied; indeed, both will be disposed to lust after strange embraces, and thus they will be led by adultery into quarrels, murders, and other deadly sins, all of which may be avoided by studying and bearing in mind the Chandrakalá.

1 Chandrakala is properly a digit, or one-sixteenth of the lunar orb.

Passion resides in the woman's right side during the
Shuklapkshá, the first or light fortnight of the lunar

GENERAL TABLE III.

Shuklapakshá or light fortnight; right side.		The touches by which passion is satisfied	Krishnapakshá or dark fortnight; left side.	
Day	Place		Place	Day
15th	Head and hair	Hold hair, and caress the head and finger-tips	Head and hair	1st
14th	Right eye	Kiss and fondle	Left eye	2nd
13th	Lower lip	Kiss, bite and chew softly	Upper lip	3rd
12th	Right cheek	Do.	Left cheek	4th
11th	Throat	Scratch gently with nails	Throat	5th
10th	Side	Do.	Side	6th
9th	Breasts	Hold in hands and gently knead	Breasts	7th
8th	All bosom	Tap softly with base of fist	All bosom	8th
7th	Navel	Pat softly with open palm	Navel	9th
6th	Nates	Hold, squeeze and tap with fist	Nates	10th
5th	Yoní	Work with friction of Linga	Yoní	11th
4th	Knee	Press with application of knee and fillip with finger	Knee	12th
3rd	Calf of leg	Press with application of calf and fillip with finger	Calf and leg	13th
2nd	Foot	Press with toe, and thrust the latter	Foot	14th
1st	Big toe	Do.	Big toe	15th

month, from new moon to full, including the fifteenth day. The reverse is the case on the dark fortnight, including its first day, and lasting from the full to the new moon. The shifting is supposed to take place by the action of light and darkness, otherwise the site of passion would be one and the same.

Now from generals, Kalyana-Malla, the poet, proceeds to particulars, and supplies details concerning the four different classes of women. He begins with the Padminí, and shows, firstly, in what limb or member passion resides; and, secondly, by what process it can be satisfied. The husband must continue his action till he sees the body-hair bristle, and hears the Sítkára[1]—the inarticulate sound produced by drawing in the air between closed teeth. Thus he will know that the paroxysm has taken place, and the beloved one is thoroughly satisfied.

[1] Called Sitkâra from the sound "S't! s't! s't! s't!" as a person breathing hard or drawing in cold air between the teeth, thus making an inarticulate sound. Full particulars concerning it will be found in Chapter IX.

TABLE IV.

Showing the Manipulations of the Padimí.

Member	Pratipadá 1st day	Dvitiyá 2nd day	Chaturthí 4th day	Panchamí 5th day
Throat	Hug with force	,,	,,	,,
Cheek	Kiss and scratch	Kiss and scratch	,,	,,
Hair	,,	,,	,,	Stroke slowly with right hand
Waist	Apply nails and scratch	,,	,,	,,
Breast	,,	,,	Scratch gently	,,
Back	Scratch and tap with fist	,,	,,	,,
Bosom	,,	Press with nails	Squeeze and knead	Press and rub
Side	Scratch and press with nails	,,	,,	,,
Thigh	,,	Scratch and press with nails	,,	,,
Belly	Scratch and press with nails	,,	,,	,,
Arm	,,	,,	Jerk suddenly and twitch	,,
Lip	Bite softly	Kiss	Bite softly and suck	Bite softly
Nipple	,,	,,	,,	Kiss, pinch softly and rub with thumb and forefinger
Space between eyes	Kiss	,,	,,	,,
Foot	,,	Scratch and press with nails	,,	,,

TABLE V.

Showing the Manipulation of the Chritrini.

Member	Shastí 6th day	Ashtamí 8th day	Dashamí 15th day	Dwádashí 12th day
Yoni	,,	Insert Linga	Rub and scratch with left hand	,,
Lower lip	Kiss	,,	,,	Bite gently
Throat	Embrace	Clasp firmly with hands	Scratch, and pass fingers over it	Embrace firmly
Waist	Scratch and press with nails	,,	Pass left hand over it and rub	,,
Navel	,,	Pinch with nails and fingers	,,	,,
Lip	,,	Bite quickly & repeatedly	,,	,,
Breast	,,	Hold in hand	Pass left hand over it and rub	,,
Ear	,,	,,	Caress with left hand	Set nails upon it
Thigh	,,	,,	Rub with left hand	,,
Middle of body	,,	,,	Pass left hand over it and rub	,,
Back	,,	,,	Rub with left hand and tap with fist	,,
Nates	,,	,,	,,	,,
Forehead	,,	,,	Kiss strongly	,,
Chest	,,	,,	,,	Kiss and pat
Eye	,,	,,	,,	Do something to make the eyes close rapidly
Hair	,,	,,	,,	Pull gently

TABLE VI.

Showing the Manipulation of the Shankhini.

Member	Tritiyá 3rd day	Saptamí 7th day	Ekadashí 11th day	Trayodashí 13th day
Body generally	twist it about	Embrace firmly	Clasp with force	,,
Lower lip	Bite	,,	,,	,,
Arm	?	,,	,,	,,
Breasts	Scratch roughly till marks are left	,,	,,	Squeeze till she makes the sound of Sítkára
Belly	,,	Scratch and press with nails	,,	,,
Chest	,,	Press with nails and caress	,,	,,
Throat	,,	Scratch and press with nails	,,	,,
Ear	,,	Press with nails	,,	,,
Foot	,,	Press so as to leave nailmarks	,,	,,
Mouth or face	,,	Kiss	,,	,,
Yoní	,,	Apply Linga with force	Apply Linga as it were with a blow[1]	,,
Lip	,,	,,	Kiss and suck	,,
Inch below head	,,	,,	,,	Write upon it, as it were, with nails
Lower edge of Yoní	?	,,	,,	,,

[1] In the original Sanskrit and in all translations there is an allusion to the practice described by Juvenal (IX. 4.).

Ravola dum Rhodopes udá terit inguina barbâ.

TABLE VII.
Showing the Manipulation of the Hastiní.

Member	Navamí 9th day	Chaturdashí 14th day	Púrnimá Full Moon	Amávásyá New Moon
Yoní	Thrust violently with Linga or even rub hard with hand	Scratch, press in member till her waist bends	,,	Manipulate & pull open like a flower
Navel	Rub and frequently pass hand over	,,	,,	,,
Lip	Kiss and suck	,,	Kiss in various ways[1]	Kiss in various ways
Side	Press with fingers and scratch very softly	,,	,,	,,
Breast	Rub, twist squeeze, & make it very small	,,	Pull hard	Scratch till it bears nail-marks
Chest	,,	,,	Scratch and leave marks	Scratch and leave marks
Nipple	,,	,,	Kiss and rub with thumb & fore-finger	Pass hand over it & rub with thumb & fore-finger
Body generally	,,	,,	Embrace in various ways	Embrace in various ways and press
Eye	,,	Kiss	Kiss	Kiss
Armpit	,,	,,	Scratch and tickle	Scratch and tickle

Here end the tables of the Chandrakalá, by the proper study of which men may satisfy women, and thereby subject the most strong-minded to their will.

[1] Alluding to what Shakespeare calls "kissing with th' inner lip."

CHAPTER III.

Of the different kinds of Men and Women.

SECTION I.

Men.

THERE are three kinds of men, namely, the Shasha, or the Hare-man; the Vrishabha, or Bull-man, and the Ashwa, or Horse-man.[1] These may be described by explanation of their nature, and by enumeration of their accidents.

The Shasha is known by a Linga which in erection does not exceed six finger-breadths, or about three inches. His figure is short and spare, but well-proportioned in shape and make; he has small hands, knees, feet, loins and thighs, the latter being darker than the rest of the skin. His features are clear and well proportioned; his face is round, his teeth are short and fine, his hair is silky, and his eyes are large and well-opened. He is of a quiet disposition; he does good for virtue's sake; he looks forward to making a name; he is humble in demeanor; his appetite for food is small, and he is moderate in carnal

---

1 These divisions again appear to represent the nervous, bilious and sanguine temperament. Some MSS. divide men only by the three Linga-lengths of 6, 9 and 12 finger breadths: the latter (6 widths) would be of African or Negro dimensions.

desires. Finally, there is nothing offensive in his Káma-salila or semen.

The Vrishabha is known by a Linga of nine fingers in length, or four inches and a-half. His body is robust and tough, like that of a tortoise; his chest is fleshy, his belly is hard, and the frogs of the upper arms are turned so as to be brought in front. His forehead is high, his eyes large and long, with pink corners, and the palms of his hands are red. His disposition is cruel and violent, restless and irascible, and his Káma-salila is ever ready.

The Ashwa is known by a Linga of twelve fingers, or about six inches long. He is tall and large-framed, but not fleshy, and his delight is in big and robust women, never in those of delicate form. His body is hard as iron, his chest is broad, full, and muscular; his body below the hips is long, and the same is the case with his mouth and teeth, his neck and ears; whilst his hands and fingers are remarkably so. His knees are somewhat crooked, and this distortion may also be observed in the nails of his toes. His hair is long, coarse and thick. His look is fixed and hard, without changing form, and his voice is deep like that of a bull. He is reckless in spirit, passionate and covetuous, gluttonous, volatile, lazy, and full of sleep. He walks slowly, placing one foot in front of the other. He cares little for the venereal rite, except when the spasm approaches. His Káma-salila is copious, salt, and goat-like.

Section II.

Women.

And as men are divided into three classes by the length of the Linga, so the four orders of women, Padminí, Chitriní, Shankhiní, and Hastiní, may be subdivided into three kinds, according to the depth and extent of the Yoní. These are the Mrigi, also called Hariní, the Deer-woman; the Vadavá or Ashviní, Mare-woman; and the Kariní, or Elephant-woman.

The Mrigi has a Yoní six fingers deep. Her body is delicate, with girlish aspect, soft and tender. Her head is small and well-proportioned; her bosom stands up well; her stomach is thin and drawn in; her thighs and Mons Veneris are fleshy, and her build below the hips is solid, whilst her arms from the shoulder downwards are large and rounded. Her hair is thick and curly; her eyes are black as the dark lotus-flower; her nostrils are fine; her cheeks and ears are large; her hands, feet, and lower lip are ruddy, and her fingers are straight. Her voice is that of the Kokila bird, and her gait the rolling of the elephant. She eats moderately, but is much addicted to the pleasures of love; she is affectionate but jealous, and she is active in mind when not subdued by her passions. Her Káma-salila has the pleasant perfume of the lotus-flower.

The Vadvá or Ashviní numbers nine fingers depth. Her body is delicate; her arms are thick from the shoulders downwards; her breasts and hips are broad and fleshy, and her umbilical region is high-raised, but without protuberant stomach. Her hands and feet are red like flowers, and well-proportioned. Her head slopes forwards and is covered with long and straight hair; her forehead is retreating; her neck is long and much bent; her throat, eyes, and mouth are broad, and her eyes are like the petals of the dark lotus. She has a graceful walk, and she loves sleep and good living. Though choleric and versatile, she is affectionate to her husband; she does not easily arrive at the venereal spasm, and her Káma-salila is perfumed like the lotus.

The Kariní has a Yoní twelve fingers in depth. Unclean in her person, she has large breasts; her nose, ears, and throat are long and thick; her cheeks are blown or expanded; her lips are long and bent outwards (bordés); her eyes are fierce and yellow-tinged; her face is broad; her hair is thick and somewhat blackish; her feet, hands, and arms are short and fat; and her teeth are large and sharp as a dog's. She is noisy when eating; her voice is hard and harsh; she is gluttonous in the extreme, and her joints crack with every movement. Of a wicked and utterly shameless disposition, she never hesitates to commit sin. Excited and disquieted by carnal desires, she is not easily satisfied, and requires congress unusually protracted. Her Káma-salila is very abundant, and it suggests the juice which flows from the elephant's temples.

The wise man will bear in mind that all these characteristics are not equally well defined, and their proportions can be known only by experience. Mostly the temperaments are mixed; often we find a combination of two and in some cases even of three. Great study, therefore, is required in judging by the absence or presence of the signs and symptoms, to choose the Chandrakalá and other manipulations proper to the several differences, as without such judgment the consequences of congress are not satisfactory. Thus the student is warned that the several distinctions of Padmaní, Chitriní, Shankhiní and Hastiní; of Shastra, Vrishabha, and Ashva, and of Mrigí (Hariní) Vadvá (Ashviní), and Kariní are seldom found pure, and that it is his duty to learn the proportions in which they combine.

Before proceeding to the various acts of congress, the symptoms of the orgasm in women must be laid down. As soon as she commences to enjoy pleasure, the eyes are half closed and watery; the body waxes cold; the breath after being hard and jerky, is expired in sobs or sighs; the lower limbs are limply stretched out after a period of rigidity; a rising and outflow of love and affection appear, with kisses and sportive gestures; and, finally, she seems as if about to swoon. At such time, a distaste for further embraces and blandishments becomes manifest: then the wise know that, the paroxysm having taken place, the woman has enjoyed plenary satisfaction; consequently, they refrain from further congress.

SECTION III.

Of Congress.

MEN and women, being, according to the above measurements, of three several divisions, it results that there are nine conditions under which congress takes place. Of these, however, four, being unusual, may be neglected, and attention is required only for the five following:

1. Samána is when the proportions of both lovers are alike and equal; hence there is plenary satisfaction to both.

2. Uchha is that excess of proportion in the man which renders congress hard and difficult and therefore does not content the woman.

3. Nichha, meaning literally *hollow* or *low*, and metaphorically when the man is deficient in size, gives but little contentment to either lover.

4. Anti-uchha is an exaggeration of Uchha; and

5. Anti-nichha is an exaggeration of Nichha.

The following table divides the congress of the several dimensions into three categories, which are respectively entitled Uttama, the best; Madhyama, the middling; and Kanishtha, the worst.

TABLE VIII.

Applicable to the Shasha, or Hare-man.

Dimensional names.	Actual dimensions of members.	Category.
Shasha Mrigí	6 fingers long 6 fingers deep	Uttama
Shasha Vadvá or Ashviní	6 fingers long 9 fingers deep	Madhyama
Shasha Kariní	6 fingers long 12 fingers deep	Kanishtha

TABLE IX.

Applicable to the Vrishabha, or Bull-man.

Dimensional Names.		Actual dimensions of members.	Category.
Vrishabha Ashvini	}	9 fingers long 9 fingers long	Uttama
Vrishabha Harini	}	9 fingers long 6 fingers deep	Madhyama
Vrishabha Karini	}	9 fingers long 12 fingers deep	Kanishtha

TABLE X.

Applicable to the Ashva, or Horse-man.

Dimensional Names.		Actual dimensions of members.	Category.
Ashva Karini	}	12 fingers long 12 fingers deep	Uttama
Ashva Ashvini	}	12 fingers long 9 fingers deep	Madhyama
Ashva Harini	}	12 fingers long 6 fingers deep	Kanishtha

From an inspection of these tables, it is abundantly evident that the greatest happiness consists in the correspondence of dimensions, and that the discomfort increases with the ratio of difference. And of this fact the reason is palpable.

There are three species of vermicules bred by blood in the Yoní,[1] and these are either Sŭkshma (small), Madhyama (middling), or Adhikabala (large). In their several proportions they produce a prurience and a titillation, wherefrom springs that carnal desire which is caused to cease only by congress. And thus it is that a Linga of small dimensions fails to satisfy. On the other hand, excess of length offends the delicacy of the parts, and produces pain rather than pleasure. But the proportion of enjoyment arises from the exact adaption of the Linga, especially when the diameter agrees with the extension, and when the vigour of tension enables the husband to turn his mind towards the usual arts which bring women under subjection.

Section IV.

Of other minor distinctions in Congress.

Each of the foregoing nine forms of congress is subdivided into nine other classes, which will now be noticed.

There are three forms of Vissrishtí, or the emission of Káma-salila, both in men and women, viewed with respect to length or shortness of time,—

1. Chirasambhava-vissrishtí is that which occupies a great length of time.

2. Madhyasambhava-vissrishtí is that which is accomplished within a moderate period.

3. Shíghrasambhava-vissrishtí is that which takes a short time to finish.

[1] A fair anticipation of the spermatozoa: see terminal note of Chapt. iv.

Again, there are three degrees of Vega, that is to say, force of carnal desire, resulting from mental or vital energy and acting upon men and women. In order to make this clear, a comparison may be instituted. Hunger for instance, is felt by all human beings, but it affects them differently. Some must satisfy it at once, without which they are ready to lose their senses; others can endure it for a moderate extent, whilst others suffer from it but little. The Vega, or capacities of enjoyment, are—

1. Chanda-vega, furious appetite or impulse; the highest capacity.

2. Madhyama-vega, or moderate desires.

3. Manda-vega, slow or cold concupiscence; the lowest capacity.

The woman who possesses Chanda-vega, may be known by her ever seeking carnal enjoyment; she must enjoy it frequently and she will not be satisfied with a single orgasm. If deprived of it, she will appear like one out of her senses. The reverse is she who has Manda-verga, and who seems to find in it so little enjoyment that she always denies herself to her husband. And the owner of Madhyana-vega is the most fortunate, as she is free from either excess.

Again, there are three Kriyás, acts or processes which brings on the orgasm in men and women; these are,—

1. Chirodaya-kriyá, is applied to the efforts which continue long before they bear any result.

2. Madhyodaya-kriyá, those which act in a moderate time.

3. Laghŭdaya-kriyá, the shortest.

Thus we may observe there are nine several forms of congress, according to the length and depth of the organs. There are also nine, determined by the longer or shorter period required to induce the orgasm, and there are nine which arise from the Kriyás or processes which lead to the conclusion. Altogether we have twenty-seven kinds of congress, which, by multiplying the nine species and the three periods, give a grand total of two hundred and forty-three ($9 \times 9 = 81 \times 3 = 243$).

CHAPTER IV.

Description of the general qualities, characteristics, temperaments, etc., of Women.

———

THE following table will show the peculiarities of women according to the four periods of life during which she is open to love. It may be premised that she is called Kanyá from birth to the age of eight years, which is the time of Bályavasthá, or childhood; and Gaurí, after the white goddess Parvati, from that period to her eleventh year; Tarŭnyavastha, when she becomes marriageable: then follow Yavavastha, young-womanhood, and Vreuddhavastha, old-womanhood.

TABLE XI.

Showing qualities attached to the several Ages.

Age	Name	Regarding art of love	Kind of Congress preferred	How subjected
11—16 years	Bálá	Fit	In darkness	By flowers, small presents, gifts of betel, and so forth
16—30 years	Taruní	Do.	In light	By gifts of dresses, pearls and ornaments
30—55 years	Praudhá	Fit (?)	Both in darkness and light	By attention, politeness, kindness and love
Beyond 55 years	Viddhá	Unfit	Becomes sick and infirm	By flattery

And further observe that there are three temperaments of women, as shown by the following characteristics:—

The signs of Kapha (lymphatic or phlegmatic diathesis) are bright eyes, teeth and nails; the body is well preserved, and the limbs do not lose their youthful form. The Yoní is cool and hard, fleshy, yet delicate; and there is love and regard for the husband. Such is the lympathic, or the highest temperament.[1]

The next is the Pitta, or bilious diathesis. The woman whose bosom and nates are flaccid and pendant, not orbiculate; whose skin is white, whilst her eyes and nails are red; whose perspiration is sour, and whose Yoní is hot and relaxed; who is well versed in the arts of congress,

[1] In old European physiology it ranked lowest.

but who cannot endure it for a long time, and whose
temper is alternately and suddenly angry and joyous, such
a one is held to be of the Pitta or bilious temperament.

She whose body is dark, hard, and coarse; whose eyes
and finger nails are blackish, and whose Yoní, instead
of being smooth, is rough as the tongue of a cow; she
whose laugh is harsh; whose mind is set on gluttony; who
is volatile and loquacious, whilst in congress she can
hardly be satisfied, that woman is of the Váta or windy
temperament, the worst of all.

Furthermore, women require to be considered in connection with the previous state of their existence; the
Satva, or disposition inherited from a former life, and
which influences their wordly natures.

The Devasatva-strí, who belongs to the Gods, is cheerful and lively, pure-bodied and clean, with perspiration
perfumed like the lotus-flower; she is clever, wealthy and
industrious, of sweet speech and benevolent, always delighting in good works; her mind is sound as her body,
nor is she ever tired of or displeased by her friends.

The Gandharvasarva-strí, who derives a name from the
Gandharvas, or heavenly minstrels, is beautiful of shape,
patient in mind, delighting in purity; wholly given to perfumes, fragrant substances and flowers, to singing and
playing, to rich dress and fair ornaments, to sport and
amorous play, especially to the Vilása, one of the classes
of feminine actions which indicate the passion of love.

The Yakshasatva-strí, who derives a name from the
demi-god presiding over the gardens and treasures of

1 The Hindu Plutus, god of wealth.

Kuvera,[1] has large and fleshy breasts, with a skin fair as the white champa-flower (*michelia champac*); she is fond of flesh and liquor; devoid of shame and decency; passionate and irascible, and at all hours greedy for congress.

The Munushyasatva-strí, who belongs essentially to humanity, delights in the pleasures of friendship and hospitality. She is respectable and honest; her mind is free from guile, and she is never wearied of religious actions, vows, and penances.

The Pisáchasatva-strí, who is concerned with that class of demons, has a short body, very dark and hot, with a forehead ever wrinkled; she is unclean in her person, greedy, fond of flesh and forbidden things, and, however much enjoyed she is ever eager of congress, like a harlot.

The Nágasatva-strí, or snake-woman, is always in hurry and confusion; her eyes look drowsy; she yawns over and over again, and she sighs with deep-drawn respiration; her mind is forgetful and she lives in doubt and suspicion.

The Kákasatva-strí, who retains the characteristics of the crow, ever rolls her eyes about as if in pain; throughout the day she wants food; she is silly, unhappy and unreasonable, spoiling everything that she touches.

The Vánarasatva-strí, or monkey-woman, rubs her eyes throughout the day, grinds and chatters with her teeth, and is very lively, active, and mercurial.

The Kharasatva-strí, who preserves the characteristics of the ass,[1] is unclean in her person, and aviods bathing,

1 The Semitic races domesticated the ass, and recognized its admirable qualities; they treated it with due respect, and they were not ashamed of being compared with it—e. g., "Issachar is a

washing, and pure raiment; she cannot give a direct answer, and she speaks awkwardly and without reason, because her mind is crooked. Therefore she pleases no one.

The subject of the Satvas is one requiring careful study, for the characteristics are ever varying, and only experience can determine the class to which women belonged in the former life, and which has coloured their bodies and minds in this state of existence.

The woman whose bosom is hard and fleshy, who appears short from the fullness of her frame, and looks bright and light-coloured, such an one is known to enjoy daily congress with her husband.

The woman who, being thin, appears very tall and somewhat dark, whose limbs and body are unenergetic and languid, the effect of involuntary chastity, such an one is "Virahiní," who suffers from long separation from her husband and from the want of conjugal embraces.

A woman who eats twice as much as a man, is four times more reckless and wicked, six times more resolute and obstinate, and eight times more violent in carnal desire. She can hardly control her lust of congress, despite the shame which is natural to the sex.

The following are the signs by which the wise know that woman is amorous:—She rubs and repeatedly

strong ass." The early Egyptian kings (B. C. 4000-1000) had no horses in their invading hosts, and the law of Moses seems to condemn the use. The "Equus Caballus" was conquered and utilized by the Caucasians in Central Asia, and they overwhelmed its rival with abuse and contempt, attributing its creation to Vishvakarma, who caricatured the work of the gods.

smoothes her hair (so that it may look well). She scratches her head (that notice may be drawn to it). She strokes her own cheeks (so as to entice her husband). She draws her dress over her bosom, apparently to read-just it, but leaves her breasts partly exposed. She bites her lower lip, chewing it, as it were. At times she looks ashamed without a cause (the result of her own warm fancies), and she sits quietly in the corner (engrossed by concupiscence). She embraces her female friends, laughing loudly and speaking sweet words, with jokes and jests, to which she desires a return in kind. She kisses and hugs young children, especially boys. She smiles with one cheek, loiters in her gait, and unnecessarily stretches herself under some pretence or other. At times she looks at her shoulders and under her arms. She stammers, and does not speak clearly and distinctly. She sighs and sobs without reason, and she yawns whenever she wants tobacco, food, or sleep. She even throws herself in her husband's way and will not readily get out of his path.

The following are the eight signs of indifference to be noted in womankind:—When worldly passion begins to subside, the wife does not look straight between her husband's eyes. If anything be asked of her, she shows unwillingness to reply. If the man draw near her, and looks happy, she feels pained. If he departs from her she shows symptoms of satisfaction. When seated upon the bedstead, she avoids amatory blandishments and lies down quietly to sleep. When kissed or toyed with she jerks away her face or her form. She cherishes malicious feelings towards her husband's friends; and finally, she has no respect nor reverence for his family. When these signs are seen, let it be known that the wife is already weaned from conjugal desires.

The following are the principal causes which drive women to deviate from the right way, and to fall into the society of profligates:—1. Remaining, when grown up, in her Máher, or mother's house, as opposed to that of her husband's parents. 2. Evil communication with the depraved of her own sex. 3. The prolonged absence of her husband. 4. Living in the society of vile and licentious men. 5. Poverty and the want of good food and dress. 6. Mental trouble, affliction, and unhappiness, causing her to become discontented and reckless.

The following are the fifteen principal causes which make women unhappy:—1. The parsimony of parents and husbands, because the youth are naturally generous. 2. Receiving too much respect or reverence when they are light-hearted; also being kept in awe by those with whom they would be familiar, and too strict restraint as regards orderly and guarded deportment. 3. Trouble of disease and sickness. 4. Separation from the husband and the want of natural enjoyment. 5. Being made to work too hard. 6. Violence, inhumanity, and cruelty, such as beating. 7. Rough language and abuse. 8. Suspicion that they are inclined to evil. 9. Intimidation and threats of punishment for going astray. 10. Calumny, accusing of ill deeds, and using evil words about them. 11. Want of cleanliness in person or dress. 12. Poverty. 13. Grief and sorrow. 14. Impotence of the husband. 15. Disregard of time and place in the act of love.

The following are the twelve periods when women have the greatest desire for congress, and at the same time are most easily satisfied:—1. When tired by walking and exhausted with bodily exercise. 2. After a long want of intercourse with the husband, such as in the case of the Virahiní. 3. When a month after childbirth has elapsed. 4. During the earlier stages of pregnancy. 5. When dull, idle and sleepy. 6. If recently cured of fever. 7. When showing signs of wantoness or bashfulness. 8. When feeling unusually merry and happy. 9. The Ritu-snátá, immediately before and after the monthly ailment.[1] 10. Maidens enjoyed for the first time. 11. Throughout the spring season. 12. During thunder, lightning and rain. At such times women are easily subjected to men.

And, furthermore, learn that there are four kinds of the Príti, or love-tie connecting men and women:—

1. Naisargikí-príti is that natural affection by which husband and wife cleave to each other like the links of an iron chain. It is a friendship amongst the good of both sexes.

2. Vishaya-príti is the fondness born in the woman, and increased by means of gifts, such as sweetmeats and delicacies, flowers, perfumery, and preparations of sandal-wood, musk, saffron, and so forth. It partakes, therefore, of gluttony, sensuality and luxury.

3. Sama-príti is also so far sensual, as it arises from the equally urgent desires of both husband and wife.

4. 'Abhyásiki-príti is the habitual love bred by mutual

1 Rítu-snátá is the woman, who, on the fourth day, has bathed and become pure.

socitey: it is shown by walking in fields, gardens and similar places; by attending together at worship, penances and self-imposed religious observances; and by frequenting sportive assemblies, plays and dances, where music and similar arts are practised.

And, moreover, let it be noted, that the desires of the woman being colder,[1] and slower to rouse than those of the man, she is not easily satisfied by a single act of congress; her lower powers of excitement demand prolonged embraces, and if these be denied her, she feels aggrieved. At the second act, however, her passions being thoroughly aroused, she finds the orgasm more violent, and then she is thoroughly contented. This state of things is clean reversed in the case of the man, who approaches the first act burning with love-heat, which cools during the second, and which leaves him languid and disinclined for a third. But the wise do not argue therefrom, that the desires of the woman, as long as she is young and strong, are not the full as real and urgent as those of the man. The custom of society and the shame of the sex may compel her to conceal them and even to boast that they do not exist; yet the man who has studied the Art of Love is never deceived by this cunning.

And here it is necessary to offer some description of the Yoní; it being of four kinds.

1. That which is soft inside as the filaments (pollen?) of the lotus-flower; this is the best.

---

1 This is the Hindu view: The Moslems hold that the desires of a woman are ten times stronger than those of a man. Both are right in certain exceptions; for instance the male is the stronger in dry climates, the female in the hot, damp and depressing.

2. That whose surface is studded with tender flesh-knots and similar rises.

3. That which abounds in rolls, wrinkles, and corrugations; and,

4. That which is rough as the cow's tongue; this is the worst.

Moreover, in the Yoní there is an artery called Saspanda; which corresponds with that of the linga, and which, when excited by the presence and energetic action of the latter, causes Káma-salila to flow. It is inside and towards the navel, and it is attached to certain roughnesses (thorns), which are peculiarly liable to induce the paroxysm when subjected to friction. The Madanachatra (the clitoris)[1] in the upper part of the Yoní, is that portion which projects like the plantain-shoot sprouting from the ground; it is connected with the Mada-váhi (sperm-flowing) artery, and causes the latter to overflow. Finally, there is an artery, termed Pŭrna-chandra, which is full of the Káma-salila, and to this the learned men of old attribute the monthly ailment.

CHAPTER V.

Characteristics of the Women of various lands.

FURTHERMORE, after dividing women into many different classes, it will be desirable to consider them with reference

[1] The "Fons et scaturigo Veneris" of the classics. It need hardly be remarked that the Hindus, like the ancients in Europe, believed the Káma-salila of women to be in every way like that of men; the microscope was required for the detection of the spermatozoa in one sex only. "Clitoris" means "shutter;" hence the French "clitoriser," to tickle it.

to the countries in which they dwell. The remarks will be confined to the Arya-varttá, the Land of Men, bounded by the Himálaya (snow-house) and Vindhya Mountains, the Kuru-Kshetra and Allahabad. And first of the woman of the Madhya-desha, the country between the Konkan and the Desha proper, whose chief cities are Puna (Poona), Nasik and Kolhapúr.

The woman of the Middle Region has red nails, but her body is still redder. She dresses well and in various sorts of apparel. She is an excellent housekeeper, perfectly broken to manual labour and other works, and much given to religious ceremonies. Though wonderfully fond of, and skilful in, amatory dalliance, she is averse to the tricks of teeth and nails (biting and scratching).

The Maru (Malwa) woman likes to be enjoyed every day, and is well fitted for those who prefer the act of congress when long protracted. She is satisfied only by enduring embraces, which she greatly covets and desires, and the paroxysm must sometimes be induced by the touch of the fingers.

The woman of Mathrá, Krishná's country, also called Abhira-deshra, the Cow-herds' Land, is fascinated by various forms of kissing. She delights in the closest embraces, and even in attouchments; but she has no tricks of tooth and nail.

The woman of Láta-desha (Lar or Larice of the Classics) the northern part of the Dakhan (Deccan), is delicate and handsome. She will dance with joy at the prospect of congress, and during the act, her movements of pleasure are frequent and violent. She is prompt in her

embraces, and the venereal orgasm may readily be introduced by gentle insertion, by striking with the hand, and
by softly biting her lips.

The woman of Andhra-desha (Telangana) is so fascinating that she charms the stranger at first sight, and
she is sweet in voice as she is beautiful of body. She
delights in jests and dalliance, yet she is an utter stranger
to shame, and she is one of the most wicked of her sex.

The woman of Koshalaráshtra-desha (Audh or Oude)
is very clever in the art of congress. She suffers much
from prurience and titillation of the Yoní, and she desires
lengthened embraces, which satisfy her only when the
Linga is of unusual vigour.

The woman of Maháráshtra (the Maratha country)
and Pátalaputa-desha is fond of giving amorous side-
glances, of dress and ornaments, of junketting and garden
trips. Ever smiling gently, airy and gay, full of jest and
sport and amorous dalliance, she is yet somewhat destitute
of shame. Affectionate and coquettish, she is a proficient
in the toying of love.

The woman of Vanga (Bengal) and Gaura has a body
soft and delicate as a flower; she is coquettish and volatile; she delights in kissing and embracing, at the same
time that she hates being roughly or cruelly handled, and
she has little desire for congress.

The woman of Utkala-desha (Orissa) is so beautiful
that man is attracted to her at first sight, and her voice is
soft as her body is delicate. She is loose and licentious,
caring very little for decency in her devotion to love, at
which time she becomes violent, disquieted and excessively

inflamed; she delights in different postures to vary enjoyment, especially in the contrary form, that is, when the lover is under the beloved, and she is easily satisfied, even by passing the fingers over her breasts.

The woman of Kámarŭpa-desha (Western Assam) has a soft body and sweet voice; her affections are warm, and she is well skilled in all the arts of love. During congress she abounds in the Káma-salila.

The Vana-strí, or forest woman (of the Bhills and other hill tribes), have stout bodies and healthy constitutions. They delight, while concealing their own defects and blemishes, their faults and follies, in exposing those of others.

The woman of Gurjara-desha (Gujrát, or Guzerat), is wise and sensible. She has beautiful features, and eyes proportioned as they ought to be; she delights in handsome dresses and ornaments, and though warm and devoted to the pleasures of love, she is easily satisfied by short congress.

The woman of Sindhu-desha (Sind), of Avanti-desha (Panjáb or Oujeín), and of Balhíka-desha (Baháwalpŭr), has lively eyes, casting sidelong and amorous glances. She is volatile, irascible, and wicked, and the fierceness, violence, and heat of her desires are very hard to be satisfied.

The woman of Tirotpatna (or Tira-desha, Tirhoot, in Central India,) has eyes blooming like the flowers of the lake; she loves her husband fondly and her passion is inflamed by a single look; she is especially skilful in congress; she enjoys various ways and postures; and, by reason of her delicacy, she cannot endure rough or protracted embraces.

The woman of Pushpapura, of Madda-desha (the north-western part of Hindostan Proper), and Tailanga-desha (Southern India), though a proficient in the art of love, is modest, and enjoys only her husband. Her form of passion is the Chanda-vega, and her amorousness is excessive; she communicates delight by "Nakhara," scratching, biting, and other signs of hot desire.

The woman of Dravia-desha (the Coromandel country, from Madras to Cape Comorin), of Sauvíra, and of Malaya-desha (Malayalim) is well-proportioned in body and limbs, soft and delicate in make, and sweet of voice; she delights in clean raiment and fine dresses, and she is satisfied with short congress, although fearless, shameless, and headlong in wickedness.

The woman of Kámbój (Camboge) and Paundra-desha is tall, robust, and gross in body, and of wicked disposition; she is ignorant of the acts of congress accompanied by tricks of nail and tooth, and she is satisfied only by the violent application of a solid Linga.

The woman of the Mlenchchhas (mixed races, or those not speaking Sanskrit like the Hindus), of Parvata, of Gandhára and of Káshm'r (Cashmere), are distinguished by evil savour of body. They are wholly ignorant of toying and dalliance, of kissing and embracing, they care little for congress, and they are easily satisfied by short embraces.

It is only by study and experience of women in different countries that the wise man learns to classify them according to their characteristics: to discern the Chandrakalás, or preparatory attouchments, which best suit races as well as individuals, and thus to endear himself to womankind.

CHAPTER VI.

*On useful Medicines, Prayogas (external applications),
Prescriptions, Recipes, Remedies, Cosmetics, Charms,
Magic, Unguents and Spells.*

———

THE following are the most useful drugs and simples, the
receipts and prescriptions which have been handed down
by learned men for the comfort of the married, and for
the benefit of the world. Also the ignorant, whose coarse
understandings cannot enter into the delicacies and intri-
cacies of classes and temperaments, of Chandrakalás, and
other excitants, are many, and they will do well to put
themselves under the guidance of the wise. This history
is intended for their pleasure and profit. It is for instance,
clearly evident that unless by some act of artifice the venereal orgasm of the female, who is colder in blood and less
easily excited, distinctly precede that of the male, the congress has been vain, the labour of the latter has done no
good, and the former has enjoyed no satisfaction. Hence
it results that one of man's chief duties in this life is to
learn to withhold himself as much as possible, and, at the
same time, to hasten the enjoyment of his partner.

FIRST PRAYOGA (EXTERNAL APPLICATION).[1]

Take Shopa, or aniseed (in Hindostani, "Sanv,"

[1] In the following prescriptions no proportions are given. It is
understood that for external applications the correct quantity is

anethum sowa or Pimpinella anisium), reduced to impalpable powder; strain and make it into an electuary with honey. This being so applied to the Linga before congress that it may reach as far inside as possible, will induce venereal paroxysm in the woman, and subject her to the power of man.

SECOND PRAYOGA.

Take cleansed seed of the Rui [1] (gigantic swallow-wort, *Asclepias* or *Callotropis gigantea,*) pound and rub in mortar with leaves of the Jai tree (*Jasminum auriculatum*, large flowered double jasmine,) till the juice is expressed; strain, and apply as before.

THIRD PRAYOGA.

Take fruit of the Tamarind (*Tamarinda Indica*), pound in a mortar, together with honey and Sindura (red lead, minium, cinnabar, or red sulphuret of mercury), and apply as before.

FOURTH PRAYOGA.

Take equal parts (Sama-bhága) of camphor, Tankan (Tincal, or brute borax, vulgarly called Tankan-khár),

the quarter of a Tola, unless otherwise specified; while those taken internally are always of a whole Tola:—

1 Masha = 15 grains = 1-12 of Tola.
¼ Tola = 45 grains = 2 scruples 5 grains.
⅔ Tola = 2 drachms = 120 grains.
1 Tola = 3 drachms = 180 grains.

1 Others translate Rúí, hogweed (Boerhavia alata diffusa).

and purified quicksilver,[1] pound them with honey, and apply them as before.

FIFTH PRAYOGA.

Take equal parts of honey, Ghí (melted or clarified butter), brute borax, as above, and juice of the leaves of the Agastá-tree (*Æschynomene grandiflora*); pound, and apply as before.

SIXTH PRAYOGA.

Take equal parts of old Gur (also called Jagri, molasses, or sugar juice, inspissated by boiling), the bean of the Tamarind-pod, and powder of aniseed; levigate with honey and apply as before.

SEVENTH PRAYOGA.

Take black pepper-corns, the seed of the thorn-apple (Dhatura or Dhotarà, *datura stramonium*), the pod of the long pepper plant (Pinpallí, the *Piper longum*, also applied to the pod of the betel pepper,) and bark of Lodhora (the *symplocos racemosa* (?), the *morinda citrifolia*, used in dyeing?) pound in white honey, and use as before. This medicine is of sovereign virtue.

Here end the prescriptions for hastening the paroxysm of the woman, and begin those which delay the orgasm of the man. In cases where this comes on too fast, the desire of congress remains unsatisfied; therefore, pitying

---

[1] The reader is strongly cautioned against this prescription, and others which contain mercury.

the frailty of human nature, the following recipes have been recommended by the wise:

FIRST PRAYOGA.

Take root of the Lajjálŭ or sensitive plant (*mimosa pudica*), and levigate with milk of the cow, or if none be found, with the thick juice of the Panja-dhari-nivarung, the fine-edged milk-plant (*euphorbia pentagonia*). If this be applied before congress to the soles of the man's feet, his embraces will be greatly prolonged by the retention of the water of life.[1]

SECOND PRAYOGA.

Take powdered root of Rúí (gigantic swallow root), levigate it in oil of safflower-seed (Kardai *carthamus tinctorius*), and apply as above.

THIRD PRAYOGA.

Take root of Káng or white panic (*P. italicum*), and the filaments (pollen?) of lotus flowers, levigate in honey, and apply as above.

FOURTH PRAYOGA.

Take equal parts of Sishu bark (the blackwood tree, *dalbergia sissoo*), camphor, and purified quicksilver; levigate as above, and apply to the (man's) navel.

[1]This process is called in Arabian medicine "Imsák," which means "holding" or "retaining". It may safely be asserted that almost every volume of the Eastern pharmacopeia is half-full of aphrodisiacs; whilst at least half the latter have for their object "Imsák". Hence, Europeans, who ignore the art and practice, are contemptuously compared by Hindu women with village cocks; and the result is that no stranger has ever been truly loved by a native girl.

FIFTH PRAYOGA.

If the seeds of the White Tál-makháná (*barleria longifolia*, a medicinal herb), be gathered upon the Pushya-nakshatra, or eighth lunar mansion[1] (corresponding with part of December and January, and be bound round the waist with a twist of red thread, it will have the desired effect.

SIXTH PRAYOGA.

Having invited (addressed with prayer), on Saturday, the Saptaparna (*echides scholaris,* or the seven-leaved

[1] The following is a useful list of the twenty-seven Nakshatras, Mansions of the Moon, or Asterisms in the moon's path:—

1. Ashviní a mare.
2. Bharaná, filling or satisfying.
3. Krittika; also the Pleiades.
4. Rohini, lightning; girl nine years old.
5. Mriga, a deer, any beast; the rain which falls during this asterism.
6. Ardra; wet.
7. Punarwasu; also called Thor-lakunwar, "great son"— i. e., an old boy.
8. Pushya (also the month Posh), which some call Tarná.
9. Ashleshá, an embrace.
10. Maghá.
11. Púrvaphalguna.
12. Uttarphalguna, the north.
13. Hasta, the hand.
14. Chittrá.
15. Sváti, solitary; also the star Arcturus.
16. Vishákhá.
17. Anurádhá.
18. Jyeshthá.
19. Múla, root, basis, origin, first ancestor, a child.
20. Púrvásháhá.
21. Uttarásháhá.
22. Shrivan, "hearing or organ of hearing."
23. Dhanistá.
24. Shata-toraká, because it contains a hundred stars.
25. Púrvabhádrapada.
26. Uttarabhádrapada.
27. Revatí, the wife of Balarám; also a kind of Chumbelí or jasmine flower.

For more concerning the Nakshatras, see Appendix I.

Scholaris), let it be taken on Sunday, and placed in the mouth; it will have the desired effect.

SEVENTH PRAYOGA.

Let a person gather the seeds of the white Anvalli (emblic myrobalan) in the Pushya-nakshatra, when it happens to fall on a Sunday, and tie them round the waist with a thread spun by a virgin; it will have the desired effect.

EIGHTH PRAYOGA.

Take the seeds of the white Tal-makháná that have been levigated in the sap of the Banyan tree (*ficus indica*), and, mixing them with the seeds of the Karanj (*galedupa arborea*), place them in the mouth, when the wished for effect will be observed.

Here end the prescriptions for delaying the orgasm of the man, and begin the Vájíkarna[1] (aphrodisiacs), which the wise of old have discovered, with a view of restoring physical strength and vigour. It is evident that the recipes given above are of no use to an impotent or to a very weak person: it is, therefore; necessary also to know the remedies which comfort the heart and excite desire, at the same time giving a power of satisfying them.[2]

[1] Váji is a horse, karan, making; applied to exciting lust by charms, etc.

[2] Most eastern treatises divide aphrodisiacs into two different kinds; 1, the mechanical or external, such as scarification, flagellation, etc.; and, 2, the medicinal, or artificial. To the former belong the application of insects, as is practised by some savage races; and all Orientalists will remember the tale of old Brahman, whose young wife insisted upon his pudendum being stung by a wasp.

FIRST VÁJIKARANA.

Having exposed the juice of the Bhúya-Kohali (the *solanum Jacquini,* a prickly plant), to the sun till dried, mix it with clarified butter, sugar-candy, and honey. This prescription gives the strength of ten men, and enables the patient to conquer ten women.

SECOND VÁJIKARANA.

Take the bark of the Anvallí (the emblic myrobalm, an astringent nut; *phyllanthus emblica*), extract the sap, expose to the sun till dried, mix with powder of the same tree, and before congress eat this powder with clarified butter, sugar-candy, and honey; a wonderful development will be the result; even an old man will become a young man.

THIRD VÁJIKARANA.

Take powder of the Kuili (Cow-itch, or *dolichos pruriens*), of the Kanta-gokhru (Caltrops, the *tribulus lanuginosus*), of the Kákri, or cucumber, of the Chikana *hedysarum lagopodioides,* of the Lechí, and of the Laghu-shatávarí (*asparagus racemosus*), and mix them in equal parts with milk; the patient will at once recover flesh and vigour.

FOURTH VÁJIKARANA.

Steep the grains of Uríd (the well-known pulse Mung, or *phaseolus radiata or P. mungo*) in milk and sugar, and expose for three days to the sun; grind it to powder, knead into a cake, fry in clarified butter, and eat every morning; the patient, though smitten with years, will gain enormous vigour, and enjoy a hundred women.

FIFTH VÁJIKARANA.

Take ten máshás (150 grains) of inner bark of the Moh tree (*bassia latifolia,* whose flowers yield a well-known spirituous liquor), rub down in a mortar, eat, and drink cow's milk upon it; the effect will be that of the preceding.

SIXTH VÁJIKARANA.

Take seeds of the White Tal-makháná and of Deva-bhat (wild rice, growing near tanks and swamps), of each ten máshás, mix with equal weight of honey, and eat at night; the effect will be the same as above.

SEVENTH VÁJIKARANA.

Mix equal parts of the juice of the Kante-shevatí (*rosa glandulifera*) expressed from the leaves, and clarified butter, boil with ten parts of milk, sugar and honey, drink habitually, and great strength of back will be the result.

EIGHTH VÁJIKARANA.

Take Loha-bhasma (a preparation from oxide of iron) powder of Triphalá (literally "the three myrobalans," *i. e.,* the yellow or chebulic myrobalan, *terminalia chébula,* the beleric myrobalan, or *terminalia belerica,* and the emblic myrobalan or *phyllanthus emblica*) and juice of liquorice (Jyestha-madh, *glycorrhiza glabra*) : mix with clarified butter and honey, and take every day at sunset; the result will be the salacity of a sparrow, a bird which enjoys the females some ten or twenty times in succession.

Here end the remedies which comfort the heart and which excite desire. But when the linga is soft or small, it is quite incapable of satisfying the wife, and of inducing her to love and to be subject to the husband. Hence it is necessary to offer recipes for thickening and enlarging that member, making it sound and strong, hard and lusty.

FIRST PRAYOGA.

Take equal quantities of Chikana (*hedysarum lago-podioides*), of Lechí, of Kosht (*costus specicosus* or *Arabicus*) of Vekhand (orris root), of Gajapimpalí (*pothos officinalis*), of Askhand (*physalis flexuosa*) in sticks, and of Kanher-root (oleander, *nerium odorum*), pound and levigate with butter, apply the result to the part, and after two ghari (48 minutes) it will assume an equine magnitude.[1]

SECOND PRAYOGA.

Take equal parts of powdered Rakta-bol (myrrh, so called because it increases the blood),[2] of Manashíl (red sulphurate of arsenic), of Costus arabicus, of aniseed[3]

---

[1] The Chinese certainly have a secret of the kind; it appears as a small pill of rhubarb colour enclosed in a waxen capsule, and as frequent analysis has shown, of vegetable matter. Dissolved in warm water and applied to the part, it produces a formication which ends in intense irritation, and greatly increases the size by inducing abnormal injection of blood.

[2] Myrrh, an invaluable gum neglected by us, appears in Hindu and Arab Pharmacopeias as a kind of universal remedy, like our books about A. D. 1500, which made one drug cure every disease.

[3] Others say Karví-Dorkí, the fruit of the cucumis acutangulus or sulcatus.

and of borax; levigate in oil of sesamum orientale, anoint the member, and the desired erethrism will follow.

THIRD PRAYOGA.

Take equal parts of Saindhava (rock salt), of pepper, of costus, of the Ringani-root (prickly nightshade), of Aghárá-filaments (*achyranthes aspera*) of Askhand (*physalisflexuosa*), of barley, of Urid (*phaselus mungo*) of the long pepper, of white Shiras (a kind of mustard), and of Til (Jingilee or *sesamum*), pound them, rub them with honey, and apply to the outer border of the ear. This medicament produces enormous growth, and, if done to a woman, it will cause the breasts to swell.

FOURTH PRAYOGA.

Take Bibvá or marking nuts (*semicarpus anacardium*), black salt,[1] and leaves of the lotus-flower, reduce to ashes, and wet these with the juice of the prickly nightshade (*solanum Jacquini*), then anoint the Linga with the egesta of the Mahishi or she-buffalo, and apply the ashes. It will immediately become larger, and strong as the wooden pestle used for pounding rice. This is considered the most efficacious prescription.

FIFTH PRAYOGA.

Mix Lodra-bark (*symplocos racemosa? morinda citrifolia?*) Hirákas (copperas, green vitrol or sulphate of

1 The "black salt" is made by fusing the fossile article in water with emblic myrobalans; it is a well-known tonic, and also used in different proportions as an aperient.

iron); Gajapimpilí (*pothos officinalis*), and Chikaná (*hedysarum lagopodioides*) with Til or sesamum oil, and apply to the Linga, when it will wax great. If done to a woman it will cause the labiæ to swell.

SIXTH PRAYOGA.

Mix Dorlí fruit (*solanum macrorrhizon*), marking-nuts, and rind of the pomegranate (fruit) with bitter oil (of the mustard, *sinapis dichotoma*, used chiefly for burning,) and apply to the part, which will be greatly enlarged.

Here end the recipes for increasing the length and breadth of the Linga, and they are followed by the inverse process of narrowing and closing the Yoní. As women advance in years, and especially after childbirth, a certain enlargement takes place, followed by softness and flaccidity of the part. Hence it is necessary to give prescriptions for rendering it small and hard, thereby increasing the enjoyment of the husband, especially when he is in the flower of life.

FIRST PRESCRIPTION.

Take the lotus, stalk as well as blossom, pound in milk, knead into small balls, and place inside the Yoní, when even a woman of fifty will become like a virgin.

SECOND PRESCRIPTION.

Take a bit of fir bark (*pinus deodaru*), and pound it with turmeric, with (Dáru-halad) (zedoary), and with the filaments (pollen?) of the lotus flower; apply internally, the result will be great constriction of the tissues.

THIRD PRESCRIPTION.

Take the pounded seed of Tal-makhâná, with the juice of the same seed, and apply inside and outside the Yoní. The effect will be instant induration.

FOURTH PRESCRIPTION.

Pound together equal quantities of the Triphala (the three myrobalans specified above), of the Dhâvâtí-flower (*grislea tomentosa*), and of the inner body of the Jámbhulí (rose-apple tree), and the Sánvarí-tree (silk cotton-tree, *bombax heptaphyllum*) with honey; apply it inside the Yoní, and the effect will be a resemblance to that of an unmarried woman.

FIFTH PRESCRIPTION.

Pound together the seeds of the Karu-bhonpalí (bitter white pompion, or pumpkin, *curcubita lagenaria*), and bark of the Lodhra-tree (*sympolocos racemosa? morinda citrofolia?*), apply them inside the Yoní and the hollowness which is felt after child birth will at once be filled up.

SIXTH PRESCRIPTION.

Take 'Askhand-shoots, Chikaná, Onvá (or Ajvini, a kind of dill or bishop's weed), zedoary, blue lotus, costus and Válá, or Khaskhas (the grass whose roots are used as "Tatties," *andropogon muricata*); mix in equal parts, pound with water, and apply internally every day; the result will be very satisfactory constriction.

SEVENTH PRESCRIPTION.

Take the salt made by boiling and evaporating the bark

of the Moh-tree (*bassia latifolia*) mix with honey, and apply it as a suppository to the Yoní, filling the latter up to its lips every day; the effect will be that of tanning.[1]

Here end the recipes for contracting and hardening the Yoní; but this part requires further treatment, and it will be necessary to offer a variety of detached recipes. The result will be to remove certain inconveniences, and to supply their place by good qualities. And first of perfuming the member, which will be given in two recipes.[2]

FIRST RECIPE.

Take oil of Shiras (a kind of mustard) and the extract from the Jáí, or Jasmine flower: let them be heated together over a slow fire, and be every day applied internally. There will be nothing unpleasant during or after the time of congress.

SECOND RECIPE.

Take a piece of pine (*pinus deodaru*), sesamum oil, Shegwa, or tree horse-radish (*guilandina moringa*), pomegranate bark, bark of the bitter Ním-tree (the Persian lilac, Caloyer tree, *melia azadiracht indica*), and flowers of the yellow Champak (*michelia champaca*); extract the oil, and apply internally, with the same result.

1 This process of contraction is universally adopted in India. Europeans who, as a rule, know only prostitutes, believe that it is effected by Chunam, or slacked lime. Of course this is a vulgar error. The popular constrictor is an infusion of astringent bark, sometimes strengthened with alum.

2 Amongst African savages the same process is effected by fumigation with odoriferous gums, which are thrown upon the fire, and the patient stands over it.

The following three Recipes will be found useful in removing and destroying the body-pile (*poil amatoire*)[1]:

FIRST RECIPE.

Place powdered oxide of lead in bitter oil; expose to sun for seven days, and apply to the "house of Smara,"[2] when all the hair will fall off.

SECOND RECIPE.

Put calcined and powdered conch-shell[3] in the juice of the banana or plantain tree (*musa paradisiaco*, and *Sapientum*); keep in the sun for seven days, and mix with a little Haritál (orpiment, yellow arsenic, or sulphuret of arsenic); then apply it to the Yoní, and all the hair will disappear.

THIRD RECIPE.

If Hartál and the shades of Palásha wood (*butea frondosa*) be levigated in the juice of the plantain-tree,

---

1 Nothing in the East is considered more impure than to wear this body-hair; it is removed by men with the razor, and by women with various depilatories, especially quicklime and orpiment in certain proportions. Even savages in the Tropics have adopted a custom, without which cleanliness cannot be. A hair of the pecten, or the axillæ, submitted to the microscope, shows excellent reason for the general practice of equatorial regions.

2 In the original, Smarálaya, from Smara, recollection, a title of Kámadeva, and Alaya, a house, as in Himálaya, which we hideously pronounce Himaláya.

3 According to others, "Shankha-Bhasma" is metallic oxide. Literally understood, it would supply lime for mixture with orpiment.

and applied to the part, no hair will ever grow again.[1]

When the monthly ailment is suddenly arrested, either by accident or disease, great evils result; and for their removal the following remedies are offered by the wise:—

FIRST REMEDY.

The woman who will levigate in water the fallen leaves of the Pingaví, or Karad-kangoní (a scandent shrub, the heart-pea, *celastrus panicolata*), and the blossoms of the Jasvad (shoe-flower,) and continue to drink it, will presently be restored to her normal state.

SECOND REMEDY.

Let a woman take equal parts of Tandul (rice),[2] Durva (Doob-grass, bent grass, or *agrestis linearis*, the well-known gramen sacred to Ganesha), and pine-wood (*P. deodaru*), reduce to powder, mix with water, and drink.

But if, on the other hand, it is judged necessary to abate the immoderate appearance of the menses, the following remedies will be found efficacious:—

[1] The great perfumers of civilized cities invariably refuse to recommend a depilatory, and it will be easily understood that the hair cannot permanently be destroyed without removing the bulb, that is to say, without excoriating the part, a painful operation, systematically performed by several savage and barbarous races. Great care must be taken in applying depilatories which contain orpiment, an active poison, that will be diffused by a scratch or a sore, and the proper proportions of lime must be added (not vaguely, as in the text), otherwise the skin will be permanently marked, or even burnt off.

[2] Others read Tandulja, an esculent vegetable.

FIRST REMEDY.

Let a woman take equal parts of Hirada-dal (bark of yellow, or chebulic myrobalans, of bitter Ním-bark,[1] and of Anwal-kathí (dried myrobalans), pound, mix with water, and drink for six successive days; the desired effect will be produced.

SECOND REMEDY.

Let a woman take equal parts of the juice of the Kapi-tya-fruit, (the elephant-apple, wood-apple or *feroni*), and of the Chivá (small bamboo), and drink it mixed with honey; she will find it equally efficacious.

The following prescriptions are invaluable for conceiving and becoming gravid, but first the field (womb) must be duly purified by the following:

PRESCRIPTION.[2]

Let a woman mix oxide of iron with calcined gold and copper, and make it into an electuary with honey; she must then eat it from the fourth (the time of bathing and

---

1 Others read Rasawati. This collyrium is prepared by boiling together calx of brass and one-eighth of Daru-haldi (curcuma xanthor-rhizon), adding to the decoction an equal part of goat's milk, and reducing (or evaporating) to one-fourth.

2 Among the people of Hindustan, Muslims as well as Hindus, there are thousands of nostrums and specifics for causing pregnancy. This is the inevitable supply caused by the demand in the harems of the wealthy, where venereal excesses and other evils which accompany riches, render want of offspring the great misery of human life. A son and heir is an absolute necessity to the Rajah and the Amir, who willingly pay enormous sums to an army of quacks and charlatans.

purification) to the sixth day after the monthly ailment, and the field will be duly cleansed.

When this is done, the following prescriptions will be found efficacious:—

FIRST PRESCRIPTION.

Let a woman take powdered Nága-kesar buds (a small Cassia, *mesua ferrea*), mix with clarified butter, and eat for three consecutive days after the fourth day, at the same time abstaining from any food but "Dughdánu," that is to say, eating anything with milk; the result of the first congress will be evident.

SECOND PRESCRIPTION.

Let a woman make a decoction of 'Askhand (*physalis flexuosa*) Gulvel (*menispermum glabrum? cocculus cordifolius?*), and of the resin called Laghu-Rál, and drink on the fourth day.

THIRD PRESCRIPTION.

Let a woman take the root of the Játwand (shoe-flower), which has been pulled up by her husband in the Pushya Nakshatra; eat it with honey, and at the same time adhere to the milk diet.

FOURTH PRESCRIPTION.

Let a woman rub down in milk the root of the Mahá-lung (common citron); boil it for a long time, and insert into it clarified butter; it must be drunk three days after the monthly ailment.

FIFTH PRESCRIPTION.

Let a woman pound the root of white Chikaná, which

has been gathered during the Pushya-Nakshatra, and mix with ten Máshás of the same root pounded, with an equal part of powdered liquorice root, and forty Máshás of sugar candy; this must be taken by the woman after the monthly impurity, in the milk of a cow which has brought forth a male calf of one colour. Nothing else must be eaten on the day of adhibiting this medicine; and, on the following day after congress with the husband at night, the woman must confine herself to rice and milk.

SIXTH PRESCRIPTION.

The woman who will continue to drink in cow's milk equal parts of dry ginger powdered, of pepper, of the long pepper, of the prickly nightshade (*solanum Jacquinia* and of cassia buds, will conceive and bear a son, no matter how long she has been barren.

Here end the medicines which result in pregnancy. But it is not enough that the woman become gravid, she must also be protected from miscarriage and other accidents. The following are the recipes to be adopted by the mother that is about to be:—

FIRST RECIPE.

Let a woman take of fine clay which adheres to the potter's hand, when he is fashioning his jar, and drink it in goat's milk. This will defend her from all injury.[1]

1 "Nothing new under the sun"—we again remark. During the last few years the use of clay externally as well as internally, in medicines as well as in surgery, has been revived, and many hospitals in the United States have preferred it as a wound-dressing to all poultices.

SECOND RECIPE.

Take equal parts of powdered liquorice,[1] Lodhara-bark and dried emblic myrobalans; these must be drunk for seven days with milk in case of the fœtus becoming misplaced, a result of the falling of the womb.

THIRD RECIPE.

Let a woman boil in milk, clarified butter, honey, and the root of the red lotus-flower; after long seething, the decoction must be allowed to cool, and it should be drunk for seven days. This medicine will prevent vomiting, irregular longings, and the vitiation of the three humours —bile, blood, and phlegm.

Here end the medicines which obviate miscarriage and accidents during pregnancy; the following are the prescriptions that ensure easy labour and easy deliverance:—

FIRST PRESCRIPTION.

Let a woman take equal quantities of powdered citron, and the bark of the Bassia latifolia, mix with clarified butter and honey, and continue to use the electuary; her travail will be light.

SECOND PRESCRIPTION.

Let a woman collect soot from the hearth or fire-place, and drink it in cold water which has been drawn the day before.

THIRD PRESCRIPTION.

Invite the Gunj or Chanotí-tree (the *abrus precatorius,* whose red and black beads are the original "carat" of the

1 Others read Prasidvá————?

goldsmith) on Saturday, pull up the root on the following Sunday, and bind it with a black thread to the woman's hair and waist.

FOURTH PRESCRIPTION.

Let a holy man recite over water the following Mantra or charm:

जय मन्मथ मथमथ बहिः लिंबाबक्ष्रोदरं मुंचमुंचलघुलघु

with whose mysteries he is familiar, and give it to the woman to drink.

Here end the medicines for ensuring easy labour. On the other hand, it may be held desirable to limit the members of the family, in which case the following prescriptions will be found useful [1] :—

FIRST PRESCRIPTION.

The woman who will eat every day for a fortnight forty Máshás of molasses (Jagri) which is three years old, will remain barren for the rest of her life.

---

[1] In a MS. I find it thus:—

ओं अग्निभार्या जयमन्मथमयमथबहिः etc., etc.

The Adi-pranava (secret word) and the Bij (literally seed, here cabalistic letter or syllable, forming the essence of the charm) are properly the ineffable "Aum" or "Om" concerning which see any treatise on Hindu Theology.

[2] The only licit way of limiting the family in India is the practice of polyandry, which is now confined to Malabar, Ceylon, and other parts of Himalayas. Abortives, however, are common throughout the Peninsula, and many women make this form of murder their trade; instruments and violence are seldom, if ever, used; dependance is placed chiefly on poisons and nostrums, consequently the mother often shares the fate of the child.

SECOND PRESCRIPTION.

Let a woman drink for three days after the fourth (purification day) a decoction of Chitraka (Ceylon leadwort, *plumbago zeylonica*) boiled with rice water.[1]

THIRD PRESCRIPTION.

The woman who will drink for three days after the fourth a decoction of the Kallambha-plant (*nauclea cadamba* or *parvifolia*) and the feet of jungle-flies, will never have children.

FOURTH PRESCRIPTION.

Levigate twenty Máshás of marking-nut (*semicarpus anacardium*), boil with Dhŭn or water in which rice has been washed, and drink for seven days, during which the monthly ailments last; the result will be life-long barrenness.

Here end the prescriptions for limiting a family. The following will be useful as cosmetics, and first of thickening and beautifying the hair :—

FIRST RECIPE.

Take flowers of sesamum (the grain), and the fruit of caltrops (*tribulus lanuginosus*), levigate in cow's milk, and apply to the hair for seven days; however thin it may have been, it will become thick and long.

SECOND RECIPE.

Levigate croton seeds (*c. tiglium*) and Sambhar or elk-horn,[2] boil in sesamum oil and apply to the hair, which

1 Others read "decoction of husks, chaff or bran of rice."
2 Others read Lodhra.

will so change its tawny colour for lamp black; and however weak and inclined to drop off it may be, it will lose all its infirmity.

THIRD RECIPE.

Rub down finely powdered Gunj-beans (*abrus precatorius*) with honey, and apply to the head; this medicament will remove the disease called "Indra-lupta-roga," or baldness of the crown.[1]

FOURTH RECIPE.

Burn ivory, pound it well, and apply it mixed with water to the head; the latter will recover hair.

Here end the prescriptions for thickening and beautifying the hair; the following are the recipes for obtaining a good black colour:—

FIRST RECIPE.

Take blossoms of the Mango-tree: the fruits of the three myrobalans, the bark of Arjuna-vriksha (Arjuna-tree, or *pentaptera arjuna*), and the rind of the penduré shrub; grind them well and boil them in sesamum oil, which now gets the name of Nílá-tel, oil of indigo—*i. e.*, of dark colour. This medicament is by far the most potent for dyeing the hair—what need I say more, except that if the wing of the Hansa (wild white goose) be dipped into it, the hue will at once take the color of night?

---

[1] What a fortune would be such a remedy in civilized lands. Yet the Hindus have something of the kind; witness the "Jatá-wálá" mendicant, who makes his hair grow upwards of six feet long and twists it round his head like a turban.

SECOND RECIPE.

Mix the powder of Persian gall-nut, long pepper, indigo leaves, and rock salt (the mordant) with sweet gruel of wheat, and the result will be a brilliant dark dye.[1]

THIRD RECIPE.

Let a man drink every day for a month forty Máshás of Ním (Melim)-tree oil;[2] his hair will gradually change colour and become glaring black as the Bhramara's wing (the "bumble-bee" of India).

FOURTH RECIPE.

Pound together Gorochana (Bezoar stones),[3] black sesamum seed, Kata-janghá (the heart pea, literally "crow's thigh") and Shatávari (*asparagus racemosus*), and apply to the hair: it will soon turn black.

For the purpose of whitening and bleaching the hair, wise men propose the following:—

PRESCRIPTION.

Wet the grain of sesamum with the juice of the Nivarung (*euphorbia pentagonia*), dry in the sun, and extract the oil; whatever part of the body is touched by this, the hair there growing will be white and bright as crystal.

---

[1] Besides black, the only dyes used in India are light sky-blue, the effect of indigo-leaves applied to the white beard by men of the Western coast, and Henna powder, which gives an orange tint.

[2] In the East there are many prescriptions to be taken internally for changing the colour of the hair; prudent men avoid them.

[3] Others translate Goro-chan, a "substance found in the cow's head" used in dying, painting and physic.

For renewing the hair of the head, there is the following :—

RECIPE.

Steep dried myrobolans in juice of the euphorbia (*pentagonia*), sun dry, pound, and apply to the hair.

It often happens that eruptions break out and leave black spots upon the face, greatly marring its comeliness. The following, therefore, are valuable prescriptions for clearing the skin :—

FIRST.

If Vekhand (orris-root[1]), elk horn,[2] and coriander-seed be pounded together and applied to the face for three days, the exanthemata which break out upon the skin of young people of both sexes, presently disappear.

SECOND.

Let a man reduce to powder the thorns of the silk-cotton-tree (*bombax heptaphyllum*), levigate it in milk, and apply it to the face: the effect will be all that he can desire.

THIRD.

Take Lodhra, rock salt, white Shiras (mustard), and Vekhand, knead with water, and rub upon the skin.

The following two recipes will remove the black colour of the epidermis and restore it to its original lighter tint :—

FIRST.

Levigate in milk, sesamum seed, coriander, Sháhá-jire

1 Others translate Vekhand by calamus aromaticus.
2 Others have Lodhra tree.

(cummin; others say *nigella indica*), and Shiras-seed; if this be applied to the body for seven days it will make the aspect clean and brilliant as the moon.

SECOND.

Take red Sanders (or sandal) wood, Tetví (the yellow wood of the *bignonia chelonoides*), root-bulbs of the sweet-smelling grass (*cyperus juncifolius*), liquorice, Tandulja (*amaranthus oleraceus*), turmeric, and zedoary; levigate with the sap drawn from crushed banana or plantain-stems, and apply to the body for seven days.

The two following are useful recipes for enlarging the breasts of women:—

FIRST.

Take shoots of 'Askhand, Vekhand, Kosht, black cummin-seed (bitter fennel?) oleander-root and cloves; pound, levigate in a mortar with water and butter; and, lastly, apply to the breasts, which will rise firm and hard.

SECOND.

Take equal parts of the kernels of the Badri (Ber, or jujube fruit, *zizyphus*), oleander-root, snake fat (?) Kankol (*myrtus pimenta*), and the heart of Jahád wood (the China cubeb tree?); pound, levigate, and use as the former prescription.

The following three recipes are invaluable for raising and hardening pendulous bosoms[1]:—

1 The women of India proper are remarkable for round and high bosoms; and the more southerly its habitat; the firmer become the breasts of the race, although we should expect the reverse, where

Boil the juice of the Narvel plant (*narwelia zeylonica*) in sesamum oil, and apply to the breasts; it will be efficacious, however flaccid they may have been.

SECOND.

Boil powder of the pomegranate fruit-rind in mustard oil, and apply to the breasts of any woman; even though she be old, they will soon become fat, fair and round.

THIRD.

Take equal parts of Rui juice (gigantic swallow-wort, *asclepias* or *callotropis gigantea*), levigate with Chikaná Tridhár (leaves of the indigo tree?), Onvá (dry ginger?), sensitive-plant, turmeric, and zedoary; and boil in sesamum oil, or in clarified butter of the cow, with great care, so that the contents of the pot may not remain raw nor be overboiled. If this ointment be placed in a woman's nostrils, the breasts will at once be drawn up. Moreover, if the same be mixed with water in which rice has been washed, and be drunk by a girl not older than sixteen, her breasts, will be enlarged and drawn up, and will never become pendulous in after-life.

It will now be right to describe the Angarág,[1] or

the climate is so distinctly hot, damp, and tropical. On the other hand, the women of Cashmere, Sind and the Panjab; of Afganistan and Persia, though otherwise beautifully shaped, and fine in face as in figure, are all more or less subject, after the birth of the first child, to the blemish of pendulous breasts. And the geographical line of sodomy corresponds with that of the flaccid bosom.

1 The following prescriptions in the original conclude the seventh, or mystical chapter. They are transferred to this place, as they evidently belong to it.

unguents, which applied to the body after ablution, naturally breed love.

Let sandal-wood, Válá (*andropogon muricatum*, vulgarly, "Cuscus") Lodhra, and mango-bark be powdered very fine, and mixed with the water of Hardá (yellow, or chebulic myrobalans). This being rubbed on the skin, will give it a charming fragrance.

The following nine recipes are useful in removing the evil savour of too much perspiration, caused by the heat of the sun, and in arresting the secretion in warm weather:—

FIRST.

Pound together, and apply leaves of the Nim and the Lodhra, with the rind of the pomegranate fruit, and bark of the Sátvani, mixed with Hardá-water.

SECOND.

Pound together the seeds of the tamarind and the Karanj (*galedupa arborea*, Roxb.; *pomgamia glabra*, Grati.; *bonducilla*, nut-tree, Grey.), and the root of the Bel tree, mixed with Hardá-water. This is sovereign for the axillæ.

THIRD.

Pound Nága-keshar, aloewood, Válá and sandal-wood, with the sap squeezed out of the inner bark of the Jujube tree.

FOURTH.

Pound together parts of the fallen flowers of the walnut tree,[1] and the fruit of the Janbali (rose apple); this arrests perspiration in warm weather.

1 Akrota-Vriksha; others read careya arborea, salvadora persica, and even a kind of palm.

FIFTH.

Pound together Nim-leaves, Lodhra, lotus-root, and pomegranate-bark; it will have the same effect.

SIXTH.

Pound the flower-filaments of the Shiras tree (*mimosa shirisa?*), Nágakesar, Válá, and Lodhra; this may either be applied to the body or eaten.

The following are sweet-smelling oils and unguents, to be used after bathing:—

FIRST.

Place Bél-leaves in sweet oil (sesamum), and expose them to the sun till dry; add successively Bakul (the flowering tree, *mimusops elengi,*) Marvá (sweet Marjorum, *origanum marjorana*), Ashoka flowers (*Jonesia asoca*) and the flowers of the Kevadá (*pandanus odoratissimus*); moisten with oil, and keep in the shade. This preparation has a surpassing fragrance much affected by the voluptuous.

SECOND.

Pound together the seeds of small cardamoms, Nágarmotha (a sweet-smelling grass) Nakhá (*unguis odoratus*, or black Byzantine), Sona-kevadá (yellow *pandamnus odoratissimus*), Jatámánsi (Indian spikenard), Kachorá (*salvia bengalensis*), and Tamál-patra (leaves of *laurus cassia*, or of *xanthochymus pictorius*); this medicament, applied to the body and hair, at bathing time, produces a delicious perfume.

THIRD.

Pound together Anvalkathí, Sona-Kevadá, Nágar-mothá, Válá, Haradá, Jatámánsí. This perfume, once applied, is capable of outlasting the fortnight.

FOURTH.

Pound together equal parts of Sandal- wood, Elá-dáná cardamom seeds), Kachorá, Tamál-patra, Haradá, and seeds or beans of the Shegva (the horse-radish tree, or *guilandina moringa* seed, *hyperanthera moringa*), with Nágar-mothá and Válá; the result will be a most odorous unguent.

FIFTH.

Pound together equal quantities of Kápŭrá (camphor), Kunkumágar (a kind of sandal wood),[1] Lodhra, Lohbán (frankincense) Válá, Nagar-motha and Kálá-válá (the dark variety of *andropogon muricatum*).

SIXTH.

Apply to the body a composition of Tamál-patra, Válá, sandal-wood, Kálá-válá, and Krishná-graŭ (black aloe-wood, *aqualaria agellochum*).

SEVENTH.

Reduce to fine powder Kastŭrí (musk), Nága-keshar, Shíla-ras (benzoin or olibanum supposed to ooze out of stone), Vishesha-dhŭp (a kind of incense, the sap of *boswellia serrata*), Ganeri-kápŭr (a kind of camphor), nutmegs and Lobhán; mix with the juice of betel leaves, and apply to the body. This perfume is fitted for Rajahs, and consequently for all other men.

1 Others translate Kunku-mágar, "saffron".

EIGHTH.

Take the following drugs in the following proportions—one part of Nágar-mothá, two parts of costus, Lehban and Kápŭr, four parts of Haradá, five parts of Shila-ras, and nine parts of Nakhlá (*unguis odoratus* or black Byzantine); this unguent is called Kástŭrí-dul (a bit of musk), and is perhaps the best fitted for Rajahs.

NINTH.

Pound together one part of Nakhlá, Haradá, Vekhand, Nágarmothá, Jatimánsí, Shopá (aniseed), and Karanj-seed, two parts of Sona-kevadá, and three parts of camphor, black sanders, musk, nutmegs and Jatámánsi; this perfume is called Sugandha-garbha; the materials are difficult to procure, consequently it is the more prized.

To the above may be added five prescriptions causing the mouth to exhale a pleasant smell.

FIRST.

Pound together Kalmí-dálchiní (a fine kind of cinnamon,) mace cardamon-grains, Nakhlá, Sona-kevadá and nutmegs; make into pills, and eat with betel leaf.[1]

SECOND.

Pound together Kesar (saffron), Kankol (the *myrtus*

---

1 Pán-supárí, the favourite "quid" of Hindostan, is composed of Pán (the leaf of the betel pepper, P. betel), containing shredded Supárí nut (the fruit of the Areca palm), with a little catechu, cardamom, nutmeg and mace, adding a small quantity of Chunám (slaked shell-lime) to bring out the flavour.

pimenia) Lohbán, nutmegs and coriander-seed, made into
pill and use as above.

THIRD.

Take for a fortnight, every morning and evening, a
powder composed of Ekangí-mura (marjoram), Nága-
kesa and costus.

FOURTH.

If carats (abrus-beans) and costus, both reduced to
powder, be mixed with honey, and be taken for a fortnight, morning and evening, the breath will be as the
perfume of the Pandanus odoratissimus.

FIFTH.

Pound the ashes of the Apámárga-vriksh (*acepranthes
aspera*), and steep in the juice of Mango-leaves; dry in
the sun and eat every morning a little of this Kshára
(alkali) with areca-nuts and betel-leaf. It is the best of
all prescriptions for purifying the breath after food.

CHAPTER VII.

Treating of Vashikarana.

VASHIKARANA is the art by which man or woman is rendered submissive and obedient to the fascinator, who for that purpose uses certain drugs and charms. And first the magic "Talaka". [1]

FIRST PRESCRIPTION.

The holy sage Vátsyáyana Muni[2] hath declared that whosoever will take the powder of sensitive plant, the root of green lotus-flowers, the Bassia latifolia, and barley-flower; and, after mixing it up with some of his own Káma salila, will apply it as a sectarian mark to his forehead, such an one will subdue the world of women, and she who looks upon his brow cannot fail to feel for him the most eager desire.

1 This is a round sectarian mark, about the size of a wafer, which the Hindu applies to his forehead, after certain rites and prayers. The reader will find this chapter interesting on account of the various abominations which it contains. The underlying idea appears to be that if any secretion of the body, the fouler the better, can be secretly administered to a person of either sex, the result is the subjection of the patient to the adhibitor. The European reader will hardly believe how extensively this practice is carried out all over the East. No Persian will drink sherbet in the house of his future mother-in-law; and Jewish women, who are especially addicted to these practices, will mix their monthly blood in the philters which they give to men.

2 The reader can now consult the Kama Sutra of the Sage Vátsyáyana, translated from the Sanskrit in seven Parts, gr. in 8vo, with Preface, Introduction and concluding remarks. (Benares, printed for the Hindoo Kama Shastra Society, 1883.)

SECOND PRESCRIPTION.

The man who will levigate the root of the giant Asclepias, the Jatámánsí, or spikenard (*valeriana Jatámánsí*), Vekhand, the sweet-smelling grass Nágar-motha (*cyperus pertenuis* or *juncifolius*), and costus with the blood from a woman's Yoní, and apply it to his forehead, shall ever be successful in the affairs of love, and shall enjoy a long course of happiness.

THIRD PRESCRIPTION.

The man who will take equal parts of Tagar (a flowering plant, *taberna montana* or *coronaria asarobacca*), of Pimpalimull (the root of *piper dichotomum*, or long pepper), of Mendha-shinghi (a plant whose fruit is compared with goat-horns or crab-claws), and of Indian spikenard; mix them together and knead them with honey, to which is added his Káma salila, or with any of the other five Mala (secretions of the body); that man will find that such a mixture applied to his forehead will enable him to overcome and subdue the women of the world.

The following recipe will enable a woman to attract and preserve her husband's love:—

Moisten Gorochana in the blood which appears every month, and apply it to the forehead as a "Tilak"; as long as it is there and the man looks upon it, so long shall he be in her power.

The following are "Anjan", or magical collyriums for winning love and friendship:—

FIRST.

Take a human skull from the cemetery or burning ground on the eighth day of the moonlit fortnight of the seventh month Ashviní (September—October), expose it to fire, and collect the soot upon a plate held over it; let this be drawn over the inner surface of the eye-lids, instead of the usual antimony, and the effect will be to fascinate every one.[1]

SECOND.

Take bamboo-manna, Nága-keshar (*messua ferrea*),[2] Korphad (*aloe perfoliata*) and Manshíla (red sulphuret of arsenic); reduce them to powder, sift, and use as collyrium; the wearer's eyes will attract the hearts of all.

THIRD.

Take wood of the Tád-palm (toddy-tree), costus, and Tagar-root, levigate in water, and with the latter moisten a piece of silk stuff; convert this into wicks with Shiras-oil, light them and take the soot formed upon a human skull in a cemetery, when held above the lamp; this is a collyrium which will make every one who looks upon it the servant or slave of the wearer.

FOURTH.

Take Manshíl, Nága-keshar, Kálá-umbar, (the fruit of *ficus glomerosa*) and bamboo-sugar, and make a colly-

[1] Nothing in Hindu eyes can be more impure or sacrilegious than such an act as this; the people having, as a rule, the highest reverence for the body from which life has departed. And the horror of the thing is, of course, the secret of its power.

[2] Others translate "Cassia buds."

rium when the Pushya-asterism falls upon a Sunday; its effect will be greatly to increase the mutual love of husband and wife.

The following three prescriptions are powerful in reducing other persons to submission:—

FIRST.

If a powder made of the Káng, or white panic (*p. italicum*), white Nishottar (*thomea turpethum*), the wing of the Bhramra-bee, costus, lotus flower, and Tagar-root, be thrown upon a man, it will at once have the effect of fascination.

SECOND.

If a powder, made of Vatálu leaves, of Soma-vallí (the moon-plant, *asclepias acida*, or *sarcostema viminalis*), and of a garland or rosary placed upon a dead body, and mingled with a little of the man's own Káma-salila, be thrown upon a person, the latter will be surely subdued.

THIRD.

If a powder, made with equal quantities of the Sáta-vina Vrisksha (the "seven-flowered tree," *astonia scholaris*, or *echites*), of the Rudrasha *eleocarpus lanceolatus*, or Ganitrus, a tree sacred to Shiva), and of the seeds of San (Bengal "sun"), be used as before, it will will have even a greater effect. This is perhaps the most potent compound for fascinating others.

A PHILTER-PILL (VATIKA).

On any Tuesday, take out the bowels of the blue jay (*coracias indica*), and let some of the fascinator's own

Káma-salila be placed inside the body; put the latter into an earthen pot, cover it with a second pot whose bottom must be turned upwards, lute with cloth and clay, and keep in a solitary place for seven days; then take out the contents[1], pound, reduce to fine powder, make pellets, or pills, and dry them. If one of these be given to a woman, she will be subject to a man, and *vice versa*.

ANOTHER CHARM.

The man who, after enjoying his wife, catches some of his own Káma-salila in his left hand, and applies it to her left foot, will find her entirely submissive to his will.

ANOTHER CHARM.

The woman who before congress will touch with her left foot the Linga of her husband, and will make a practice of this, undoubtedly subdues him, and makes him her slave for life.

ANOTHER CHARM.

Let a man take the egesta of the spotted-necked pigeon; rock-salt, and the leaves of the Bassia latifolia in equal parts, powder them, and rub the powder upon his Linga before congress, he will become the woman's master.

ANOTHER CHARM.

Let a man levigate together Kásturí (common musk, also applied to a kind of camphor) and wood of the yellow Tetu-tree; mix them with honey two months old, and apply the substance to his Linga before congress, it will have the same effect.

1 These, of course, would be putrid in an Indian climate.

A FASCINATING INCENSE, OR FUMIGATION.

Pound well together sandal-wood, Kunku (red powder prepared from turmeric and alum coloured with lemon-juice and other matters), costus, Krishna-gurŭ (black sanders), Suvásika-pushpa (perfumed flowers?), white válá (the fragrant *andropogon muricatum*) and the bark of the Deodaru pine; and, after reducing them to fine powder, mix it with honey and thoroughly dry. It is now known as Chinta-mani-Dhupa, the "thought-mastering incense." If a little of this be used according to the cere-monies prescribed, he who employs it will make all the world submissive to him.

ANOTHER INCENSE.

Pound and mix together equal quantities of cardamom-seeds, Olibanum (or gum benzoin), the plant Garur-wel Moon-seed, *monispermum glabrum*, or *cocculus cardi-folius*, sandal-wood, the flowers of the eared jasmine, and Bengal madder. This incense is powerful as that above.

The following are the Mantras, or magical versets which have the power of fascination :—

I. KAMESHWAR MANTRA[1]

कामेश्वर अमुका आनय आनय वश्यतां क्री

O Kameshwar, bring such and such a woman under sub-jection to me.

The form of use is as follows ;—Accompany the word Kámeshwar with the mystic "Om," or Pranava. Then let the woman's name precede the words, A'naya ! A'naya !

---

[1] The reader need hardly be told that even in England the old-

and follow with the Bija (the seed, or cabalistic conclusion.) The charm is to be repeated mentally 10,000 times, counted by a string (rosary) 108 Kadamba blossoms (*nauclea cadamoa*), or those of the Palasa (*butea frondosa*). The sacrifice or offering consists of burning the same kind of flowers, counting a tenth part of the number of repetition, that is to say, one thousand. Thus the Mantra-devatá is brought under our power.[2] One of the flowers, which has been charmed by this verset being recited over it, is finally given to the woman whose name has been pronounced, and thus her subjugation is effected.

2. CHAMUNDA MANTRA.[3]

चामुंडे मोहय वश्यतां अमुकीं

Repeat the Mantra mentally a lakh of times (100,000) with the pranava. Sacrifice 10,000 flowers of the Butea frondosa, at the same time offering the Tarpana[4] (or presenting water to the object of worship). When the ceremonies and works of propitiation are performed, the Mantra-devatá is subdued, and the woman is fascinated

fashioned superstition of summoning an absent person is not extinct. The formulas, as a rule, are silly verses, whose sole object is apparently to control the will of the reciter. They lead to a complicated subject, the animal magnetism, or mesmerism, both names equally absurd, which has been practised in India from time immemorial.

2 The efficacy of the Mantra is in the Devatá, or deity that resides in it, and he is conquered or conciliated by the mere act of repetition and of making offerings. This conclusion results directly from the Hindu theory of prayer.

3 Chámunda is one of the many names of Deví, the wife or Sakti of the god Shiva.

4 Literally, "satisfaction"; generally applied to the rite of offering water to the Pitris or ancestral Manes.

by a gift of a flower over which the verset has been repeated seven times.

3. THE MANTRA THAT SUBDUES THE PADMINI.

कामेश्वर मोहय मोहय खाह्रा

Repeat this Mantra, with the Pravana, till the Mantra-devatá has been mastered.[1] Then write this Kameshvara-Mantra upon a betel-leaf with the flower steeped in honey, choosing Sunday for the act. Finally, after repeating the same Mantra a hundred times, give the flower to the Padminí, who will undoubtedly be subdued.

4. THE MADANASTRA-MANTRA THAT SUBDUES THE CHITRINI.

विहंगम विहंगम कामदेवात्खै

Repeat this Mantra with Pranava (10,000—100,000 times) till the deity which it contains is mastered. Then moisten nutmeg-powder in the juice squeezed from the root of the plantain tree, place it in a roll of betel-leaf which has been charmed by repeating over it the Mantra on Sunday, and let the Chitriní woman eat it.[2] She will certainly be subjected.

---

[1] Here nothing is said concerning the number of times, which may be 10,000 or 100,000. Of course, the more repetitions the better, as thus the Mantra-devatá, without whom the formula has no efficacy, will be the more surely bound. The Muslims of India have borrowed all these superstitions from the heathen.

[2] Here the difficulty will be to persuade the women to eat the charmed betel; in the East the people are prudent in such matters, and we have seen reasons why they should be.

25

5.   THE MANTRA THAT SUBDUES THE SHANKHINI.

पचपच स्वाहा

It is said by the ancient learned men conversant with the science of fascination, that this Mantra is exceedingly efficacious. After the Mantra-devatá is subdued in the usual manner, let the root of the Tagar and cocoa-nut, or the Belfruit (*aegle marmaros*, or *crataera religiosa*, a tree sacred to Shiva) be charmed and given to the Shankhiní; if she eat any part of it, she is subject to obedience.

धिरांधिरांकामदेवाय तस्मै स्वाहा

After subduing the Mantra-devatá, pound the wing of a pigeon[1] in honey, make pills of it, and administer to the Hastiní, who will at once become fascinated.

═══════════

CHAPTER VIII.

—

Of different Signs in Men and Women.

THE characteristics of a woman whom we should take to wife, are as follows:—She should come from a family of

1 Others read Kevdá, a Francolin partridge.

2 This chapter has been left in all its original confusion of subjects; it would be easy to revise it, but then it would lose "cachet".

equal rank with that of her husband, a house which is known to be valiant and chaste, wise and learned, prudent and patient, correct and becomingly behaved, and famed for acting according to its religion, and for discharging its social duties. She should be free from vices, and endowed with all good qualities, possess a fair face and fine person, have brothers and kinsfolk, and be a great proficient in the Kama-shástra, or Science of Love. Such a girl is truly fitted for marriage; and let a sensible man hasten to take her, by performing the ceremonies which are commanded in the Holy Law.

And here may be learned the marks whereby beauty and good shape of body are distinguished. The maiden whose face is soft and pleasing as the moon; whose eyes are bright and liquid as the fawn's, whose nose is delicate as the sesamum flowers; whose teeth are clean as diamonds and clear as pearls; whose ears are small and rounded; whose neck is like a sea-shell, with three delicate lines or tracings behind; whose lower lip is red as the ripe fruit of the bryony; whose hair is black as the Bhramara's wing; whose skin is brilliant as the flower of the dark-blue lotus, or light as the surface of polished gold; whose feet and hands are red, being marked with the circular Chakrá or discus;[2] whose stomach is small, whilst the umbilical region is drawn in; whose shape below the hips is large; whose thighs, being well-proportioned and pleasing as the plantain-tree, make her walk like the elephant, neither too

1 The large black bee of Southern Europe, India, etc. Corresponding with the "bumble bee" of England, but without the yellow markings.

2 Alluded to in a future part of the chapter.

fast nor too slow; whose voice is sweet as the Kokila-bird's—such a girl, especially if her temper be good, her nature kindly, her sleep short, and her mind and body not inclined to laziness, should at once be married by the wise man.

But the girl who comes from a bad family; whose body is either very short or very tall, very fat or very thin; whose skin is ever rough and hard; whose hair and eyes are yellowish, the latter like a cat's; whose teeth are long, or are wholly wanting; whose mouth and lips are wide and projecting,[1] with the lower lip of dark colour, and tremulous when speaking; who allows her tongue to loll out; whose eyebrows are straight; whose temples are depressed; who shows signs of beard, mustachios, and dense body-pile; whose neck is thick; who has some limbs shorter and others longer than the usual proportion; whose one breast is large or high, and the other low or small; whose ears are triangular, like a sifting or winnowing fan; whose second toe is larger and longer than the big toe;[2] whose third toe is blunt, without tip or point, and whose little toes do not touch the ground; whose voice is harsh and laugh is loud; who walks quickly and

1 All Easterns uphold the doctrine of the Salernitan School. Noscitur a labiis quantum sit virginis antrum: nositur a naso quanta sit hasta viro.

2 In Europe there is much dispute concerning this canon. But the big toe represents the thumb which distinguishes the human from the simian hand, and the longer the better formed the two are, the higher is the organisation. In this matter races greatly differ: compare, for instance, the short thumb of the Anglo-Saxon with the long thumb of the Celt, or the common Englishman with the common Irishman.

with uncertain gait; who is full grown; who is disposed to be sickly, and who bears the name of a mountain (as Govardhan),[1] of a tree (as Anbí), of a river (as Tarangíní), of a bird (as Chimaní), or of a constellation (as Revatí, the 27th lunar mansion)—such a girl, especially if her disposition be irascible and temper violent; if she eat and sleep much; if she be always vexed, troubled and distressed; if her disposition be restless and fidgetty; if she has little understanding in worldly matters; if she be destitute of shame and if her natural disposition be wicked, should be carefully avoided, under all circumstances, by the wise.

So much for the characteristics of the woman. On the other hand, man should be tried, even as gold is tested, in four ways: 1, by the touchstone; 2, by cutting; 3, by heating; and, 4, by hammering. Thus should we take into consideration—1, learning; 2, disposition; 3, qualities; and 4, action. The first characteristic of a man is courage, with endurance; if he attempt any deed, great or small, he should do it with the spirit of a lion. Second, is prudence: time and place must be determined, and opportunity devised, like the Bak-heron, that stands intently eyeing its prey in the pool below. The third is early rising, and causing others to do the same. The fourth is hardihood in war. The fifth is a generous distribution and division of food and property amongst family and friends. The sixth is duly attending to the wants of the wife. The seventh is circumspection in love matters. The eighth is secrecy and privacy in the venereal act. The ninth is

1 The Hill in Mathura, which Krishna held up in hand.

patience and perseverance in all the business of life. The tenth is judgment in collecting and in storing up what may be necessary. The eleventh is not to allow wealth and worldly success to engender pride and vanity, magnificence and ostentation. The twelfth is never aspiring to the unattainable. The thirteenth is contentment with what the man has, if he can get no more. The fourteenth is plainness of diet. The fifteenth is to avoid over sleep. The sixteenth is to be diligent in the service of employers. The seventeenth is not to fly when attacked by robbers and villains. The eighteenth is working willingly; for instance, not taking into consideration the sun and shade if the labourer be obliged to carry a parcel. The nineteenth is the patient endurance of trouble. The twentieth is to keep the eye fixed upon a great business; and the twenty-first is to study the means properest for success. Now, any person who combines these twenty-one qualities is deservedly reputed an excellent man.

When choosing a son-in-law, the following characteristics should be aimed at:—He must come from a large family, which has never known sin and poverty. He must be young, handsome, wealthy, brave and influential; diligent in business, moderate in enjoying riches, sweet of speech, well versed in discharging his own duties, known to the world as a mine of virtues, steadfast in mind, and a treasury of mercy, who gives alms and makes charities as far as his means permit. Such a man is described by celebrated poets as a fit person to whom the daughter should be given in marriage.

And these are the defects and blemishes of a son-in-law;

—The man who is born in a low family, who is vicious, a libertine, pitiless, and ever sickly with dangerous disease, sinful and very wicked, poor and miserly, impotent, prone to conceal the virtues and to divulge the vices of others; a constant traveller, an absentee, one ever away from his home and residing abroad; a debtor, a beggar, a man who has no friendship with the good, or who, if he have it, breaks into quarrel upon trifling things—such a person the wise will not accept as a son-in-law.

We now proceed to the Sámudrika-lakshana or chiromantic signs, good and bad, which affect present and future happiness. The length of a man's and woman's life, and the marks which denote it, must first be treated of, because it is useless to see suspicious details if death may shortly be expected. And first of all the palmistry of the man.

Every perfect hand and foot consists of five members, namely the Angushthá (thumb), the Tarjaní (forefinger), the Madhyamá (middle-finger), the Anámiká (ring-finger), and the Kanishthiká (little finger). Now, if an

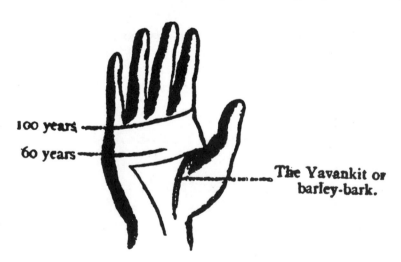

unbroken line in the palm[1] run from the "mount" or base of the little finger, to that of the forefinger, it is a sign that the bearer will live a hundred years. But the man in whose palm an unbroken line runs from the ball or cushion of the little finger to that of the middle-finger, should be considered as likely to live for a period of sixty years. Moreover, the man upon whose thumb or chest there is a figure shaped like a barley grain,[2] the same will eat bread earned by his own exertions, and he will ever remain happy. As a rule, if the lines in the palms be few, men are poor and penniless; if there be four they are happy; and if more than four, they are threatened with mean and wretched fortunes; moreover, the much streaked palm shows a quarrelsome nature.

The man whose eye is red, whose body is fair and of good complexion like gold; whose trunk is fleshy and whose arms reach his knees,[3] the same will always remain rich and enjoy grandeur, opulence, lordship and supremacy.

The man whose thighs are large, will win great wealth;

[1] As a rule the plamistry of the Gypsies is directly derived, like their language, from India, and so artificial a system speaks strongly in favour of a single origin and propagation by tradition. Here, however, the "line of life" (linea vitæ) is transferred from the base of the thumb to an unusual place, technically called the Cingulum Veneris.

[2] This figure Europeans turn into an M, and hold to mean marriage. The "barley-mark" in the text seems to correspond with the triangle formed by the "supreme natural Line," the "Line of Life," and the "Line of the Lunar Mount." (Richard Saunders' "Physiognomie and Chiromancie," London, 1671; and Les Mystéres de la Main," Ad. Desbarrolles, Paris, Dentu, 1862).

[3] Such was the case with the celebrated Highland cateran, Rob Roy Macgregor.

the man whose waist is broad, will be blessed in his wife and many children; the man whose feet are long,[1] and whose hands are very delicate, will always enjoy happiness; and the man whose head is large and lengthy,[2] will rise to be a prince.

The man whose Linga is very long, will be wretchedly poor. The man whose Linga is very thick, will ever be very lucky; and the man whose Linga is short, will be a Rajah.[3] So much concerning the characteristics of men.

And now as regards the other sex. The woman of inauspicious signs, will be, or become an orphan, a widow, destitute of brothers and sisters, and without connections, as well as relations, so that her life ends, as it began, in bitterness. Her characteristics, therefore, should be carefully examined before marriage with her is contracted.

Let it be understood that the woman who bears on the sole of her left foot the signs of the Chakra (quoit, peculiar to Vishnu), the Padma (lotus), the Dhvaja (flag), the Chatra (umbrella), the mystical Svastika,[4] and the Kamala, that is circular lines,[1] and not conch-

1 An unusual conformation in the Indian, whose short thin feet are despised by the Afghans, and the adjacent mountaineers. When Ranjit Singh ordered a hundred matchlocks from a celebrated gunsmith across the Indus, he received in return a slipper with a message that the order would be executed as soon as a Sikh's foot could be found to fit that shoe.

2 An idea long familiar to the world before the days of Dr. Gall.

3 Here we find a Hindu origin for the naughty schoolboy lines about short and thick—long and thin.

4 The Svastika is the crutched cross, known to the Scandinavians as the "hammer of Thor," and supposed to denote the thunderbolt. It is painted on doors in India as an auspicious mark or seal, and is affixed to documents in lieu of signatures by Hindu wives (not

shaped on her finger-tips, that woman will be a Rani (queen). If, however, one or more of these figures be wanting, she will enjoy all the happiness of a crowned head.

The woman who bears on the sole of her left foot a line extending from the "mount" or cushion of the little toe, to the ball of the big toe, that woman will readily obtain a good husband, and will find great happiness in his love.

The woman whose two little toes do not touch the ground whilst walking, will certainly lose her husband; and during her widowhood, she will not be able to keep herself chaste.

The woman whose Tarjaní or second toe is the longest of all the toes, will be unchaste even before marriage. What doubt, then, is there of her being an adulteress as long as her youth endures?

The woman whose breasts are fleshy, firm, and handsome, whose bosom is without hair, and whose thighs are like the trunk of an elephant, will enjoy a life of happiness.

The maiden who has black moles upon her left breast, throat and ears, will marry and bear a son having auspicious marks; and by her means, all the family will be called blessed.

The maiden whose neck is very long, will be of a wicked and cruel disposition. The maiden whose neck is very short, will be wretchedly poor. The maiden whose

widows), who cannot write their names. "Svastika," amongst the Jains, is the emblem of the seventh Gurú or spiritual teacher, and the word is also applied to a temple built in the shape of a symbol.

1 These circular lines being held particularly auspicious.

neck has three lines or wrinkles, will be of a good disposition, and her lot will be ever fortunate.

The maiden who bears in the palm of her hand lines resembling enclosing walls, and "Toran" or garlands of flowers, and twigs of trees bent into circles,[1] will become the wife of a King, although she have been born in a servant's house.

The maiden whose palms have lines in the shape of an Ankush (spiked hook for guiding elephants), a Kuntala (or spur), and a Chakra (quoit or discus), will intermarry with a royal house, and bear a son who shows the most fortunate signs.

It is written in he book Náradokta[2] that marriage should never be contracted with a girl, unless the lines and spots, as interpreted by treatises on Chiromancy, are first examined and found good. The consequence of unauspicious signs is that her birth will cause the death of her father, mother and brother in sucession. The man who marries such a maiden, will presently die, and be followed by all his brethren, and the two families will be destroyed.

There are seven kinds of troubles which result from having intercourse with the wife of another man. Firstly, adultery shortens or lessens the period of life; secondly, the body becomes spiritless and vigourless; thirdly, the world derides and reproaches the lover; fourthly, he despises himself; fifthly, his wealth greatly decreases;

1 These ornaments are hung from doorways or about awnings on festive occasions.

2 That is, the book written by Nàrada, one of the twenty Rishis or Sages, and a son of Brahma. His name is properly applied to a quarrelsome and embroiling fellow.

in thought how to woo and win the woman in question; sixthly, he suffers much in this world; and, seventhly, he will suffer more in the world to come. Yet, despite all this ignominy, disgrace and contumely, it is absolutely necessary to have connection with the wife of another, under certain circumstances, which will be presently specified.

Great and powerful monarchs have ruined themselves and their realms by their desire to enjoy the wives of others. For instance, in former days the family of the Rávana, King of Lanká (Ceylon), was destroyed because he forcibly abducted Síta, the wife of Ráma, and this action gave rise to the Ramáyana poem, which is known to the whole world. Válí lost his life for attempting to have connection with Tárá, as is fully described in the Kishkindá-kánd, a chapter of that history. Kíchaka, the Kaurava, together with all his brethren, met with destruction, because he wished to have Draupada[1] (daughter of Drupad), the common wife of the Pandu brothers, as is described in the Virát-parví (section) of the Mahabhárat. Such are the destructions which in days past have happened to those who coveted other men's wives; let none, therefore, attempt adultery even in their thoughts.

But there are ten changes in the natural state of men, which require to be taken into consideration. Firstly, when he is in a state of Dhyása (*desiderium*), at a loss to do anything except to see a particular woman; secondly, when he finds his mind wandering, as if he were about to lose his senses; thirdly, when he is ever losing himself;

---

[1] These three represent "Helen of Troy" in the classical history of Hindustan.

fourthly, when he passes restless nights without the refreshment of sleep; fifthly, when his looks become haggard and his body emaciated; sixthly, when he feels himself growing shameless and departing from all sense of decency and decorum; seventhly, when his riches take to themselves wings and fly; eighthly, when the state of mental intoxication verges upon madness; ninthly, when fainting fits come on; and tenthly, when he finds himself at the door of death.[1]

That these states are produced by sexual passion may be illustrated by an instance borrowed from the history of bygone days. Once upon a time there was a king called Purŭravá, who was a devout man, and who entered upon such a course of mortification and austerities that Indra, Lord of the Lower Heaven, began to fear lest he himself might be dethroned. The god, therefore, in order to interrupt these penances and other religious acts, sent down from Svarga, his own heaven, Urváshí, the most lovely of the Apsaras (nymphs). The king no sooner saw her than he fell in love with her, thinking day and night of nothing but possessing her, till at last succeeding in his project, both spent a long time in the pleasures of carnal connection. Presently Indra, happening to remember the Apsara, despatched his messenger, one of the Gandharvas (heavenly minstrels), to the world of mortals, and recalled her. Immediately after her departure, the mind of Purŭravá began to wander; he could no longer concentrate his thoughts upon worship and he felt upon the point of death.

1 These ten are the progressive stages of love longing.

See, then, the state to which that king was reduced by thinking so much about Urváshí! When a man has allowed himself to be carried away captive of desire, he must consult a physician, and the books of medicine which treat upon the subject. And, if he come to the conclusion that unless he enjoy his neighbour's wife he will surely die, he should, for the sake of preserving his life, possess her once and once only.[1] If, however, there be no such peremptory cause, he is by no means justified in enjoying the wife of another person, merely for the sake of pleasure and wanton gratification.

Moreover, the book of Vatsayáyana, the Rishi, teaches us as follows: Suppose that a woman, having reached the lusty vigour of her age, happened to become so inflamed with love for a man, and so heated by passion that she feels herself falling into the ten states before described, and likely to end in death attended with phrenzy, if her beloved refuse her sexual commerce. Under these circumstances, the man, after allowing himself to be importuned for a time, should reflect that his refusal will cost her life; he should, therefore, enjoy her on one occasion, but not always.

The following women, however, are absolutely, and under all circumstances, to be excluded from any commerce of the kind. The wife of a Brahman; of a Shrotíya

1 This was the heathen idea generally, and a friend would hardly have felt justified in refusing, under such circumstances, the loan of his wife. So Seleucus, King of Syria, gave the fair Stratoníke to his son, Antiochus, in order to save a life which was endangered by the violence of passion. Equally generous was Socrates, the "Christian before Christianity;" which generosity may, perhaps, account in part for the temper of Xantippe.

(Brahman learned in the Vedas); of an Agnihotrí (priest who keeps up the sacred fire), and of a Puránik (reader of the Puránas). To look significantly at such a woman, or to think of her with a view of sensual desire, is highly improper: what, then, must we think of the sin of carnal copulation with her? In like manner, men prepare to go to Naraka (hell) by lying with the wife of a Khatríya (king, or any man of the warrior caste, now extinct); of a friend or of a relation. The author of this book strongly warns and commands his readers to avoid all such deadly sins.

Indeed, there are certain other women who are never to be enjoyed, however much a man may be tempted. First, a virgin without marrying her; second, a widow;[1] third a woman living chastely or virtuously with her husband; fourth, the wife of our friend; fifth, the wife of our foe; sixth, any of the reverend women specified above; seventh, the wife of a pupil or a disciple; eighth, a woman born in one's own family; ninth, a woman afflicted with any serious complaint; tenth, a woman who has been defiled;

[1] Because by Hindu custom, if not by the old law, the lover cannot marry a widow.

[2] Easterns are all agreed upon this point, and the idea is that the embraces of a woman older than the husband, "burn" and destroy his strength. It is certain that when there is considerable difference of age, the younger of the two suffers in appearance, if not in health. How many women we see in civilized countries with that young-old look, which at once assures the observer that they are married to men much their seniors? We seldom meet in society with the reverse case, for ridicule always attaches to a man's marrying a woman whose age greatly exceeds his own. Yet the few instances which appear, justify our belief that there is something the reverse of hygienic in the practice.

eleventh, a mad woman; twelth, a woman older than oneself;[2] thirteenth, the wife of a Guru, spiritual tutor, instructor or guide; fourteenth, one's mother-in-law; fifteenth, one's maternal aunt (mother's sister); sixteenth, the wife of one's maternal uncle;[1] seventeenth, one's paternal aunt (father's sister); eighteenth, one's paternal uncle's wife; nineteenth, a sister; twentieth, a pregnant woman; twenty-first, a woman who has committed mortal sins and crimes; twenty-third, a woman whose complexion is entirely yellow; twenty-fourth, a woman whose complexion is quite black. It is laid down in the Shástras (scriptures), that the wise should never, under any circumstances, have connection with these twenty-four kinds of women, as well as with others, bearing any relationship to one.

The following is a list of the women who serve but as go-betweens:[2] First, a gardener's wife. Second, a woman who is a personal friend. Third, a widow. Fourth, a nurse. Fifth a dancing-girl. Sixth, a woman engaged in manual or mechanical arts. Seventh, a woman hired as a servant or maid to the women of the family. Eighth, an attendant as distinguished from a slave girl. Ninth, a woman who goes from house to house speaking sweet words. Tenth, a woman with whom we can talk freely about love and enjoyment. Eleventh, a young woman

1 In Sanskrit, and in the Prakrit or modern language of Hindostan, there are different names for our "aunt": Mávashi, for instance, is the maternal aunt, and Mámí, the maternal uncle's wife.

2 This need not necessarily be taken in a bad sense, as "procuress." In Hindu, as well as in Muslim families, women are sufficiently secluded to require the assistance of feminine Mercuries in matters of marriage.

under sixteen. Twelfth, a female ascetic or mendicant in the name of religion. Thirteenth, a woman who sells milk and buttermilk. Fourteenth, a tailoress. Fifteenth, a woman fit to be called "Mistress Grandmother." The amorous should prefer these kind of persons, as, when deputed upon such messages, they do their work kindly and well.

The following is a list of the women who can most easily be subdued.[1] First a woman whose deportment shows signs of immodesty. Second, a widow. Third, a woman who is highly accomplished in singing, in playing musical instruments, and in similar pleasant arts. Fourth, a woman who is fond of conversation. Fifth, a woman steeped in poverty. Sixth, the wife of an imbecile or an impotent person. Seventh, the wife of a fat and tun-bellied man. Eighth, the wife of a cruel and wicked man. Ninth, the wife of one who is shorter than herself. Tenth, the wife of an old man. Eleventh, the wife of a very ugly man. Twelfth, a woman accustomed to stand in the door-way and to stare at passers by. Thirteenth, women of variable disposition. Fourteenth, the barren woman, especially if she and her husband desire the blessing of issue. Fifteenth, the woman who brags and boasts. Sixteenth, the woman who has long been separated from her husband and deprived of her natural refreshment. Seventeenth, the woman who has never learned the real delight of car-

---

1 This can hardly be used in an honest sense: it might be translated "seduced," were not that word so liable to misuse and misconstruction. What man in his senses can believe in the "seduction" of a married woman? As a rule, indeed, the seduction is all on the other side.

nal copulation;[1] and, eighteenth, the woman whose mind remains girlish.

And now to describe the signs and symptoms by which we are to know when women are enamoured of us. Firstly, that woman loves a man when she is not ashamed of looking at him,[2] and of boldly and without fear or deference keeping her eyes fixed upon his. Secondly, when she moves her foot to and fro whilst standing up, and draws, as it were, lines upon the ground. Thirdly, when she scratches divers limbs without a sufficient reason. Fourthly, when she leers, looks obliquely, and casts side-glances. Fifthly, when she laughs causelessly at the sight of a man.

And furthermore, the woman who, instead of answering a straightforward question, replies by joking and jesting words; who slowly and deliberately follows us wherever we go; who under some pretext or other, dwells upon our faces or forms with a wistful and yearning glance; who delights in walking before us and displaying her legs or her bosom; who behaves to us with a mean and servile submission, ever praising and flatering; who contracts friendship with our friends and who is ever asking them, "In the house of such and such a person, are there any wives? Does he love them much? And are they very

1 Which, allow us to state, is the case with most Englishwomen and a case to be remedied only by constant and intelligent study of the Ananga-Ranga Scripture.

2 In the East, women take the first step in such matters. Nothing can be more ridiculous than to see the bearded and turbaned Turk blushing, "boggling," and looking silly as he is being inspected by a pair of bold feminine eyes.

beautiful? " Who, looking towards us, sings a sweet air; who passes her hands frequently over her breasts and her arms; who cracks her fingers; who yawns and sighs when not expected to do so; who will never appear before us, though we call and summon her, unless in her most becoming dress; who throws flowers and similar articles upon us; who pretexting various things, often goes into and comes forth from the house; and finally, whose face, hands and feet break into perspiration when she casually sees us; that woman showing any such signs and symptoms, is enamoured of us, and is strongly excited by passion; all we have to do, if versed in the art of love, is to send an able go-between.

On the other hand, the following women are hard to be subdued:—First, the wife who is full of love for her husband. Second, the woman whose cold desires and contempt for congress keep her chaste. Third, the woman who is envious of another's prosperity and success. Fourth, the mother of many children. Fifth, a dutiful daughter or daughter-in-law. Sixth, a courteous and respectful woman. Seventh, a woman who fears and stands in awe of her parents and those of her husband. Eighth, a wealthy woman, who ever suspects and often wrongly, that we love her money better than herself. Ninth, a woman who is shy, bashful, and retiring in the presence of strangers. Tenth, an avaricious and covetuous woman. Eleventh, a woman who has no avarice or covetuousness. Such women are not easily secured, nor is it worth our while to waste our hours in pursuing them.

The following are the places where a woman should not

be enjoyed:—First, the place where fire is lighted with the religious formula Agni-mukha and other Mantras. Second, in the presence of a Brahman or any other reverend man. Third, under the eyes of an aged person, to whom respect is due, as a Guru (spiritual guide), or a father. Further, when a great man is looking on. Fifth, by the side of a river or any murmuring stream. Sixth, at a Pánwatá, a place erected for drawing water from wells, tanks and so forth. Seventh, in a temple dedicated to the gods. Eighth, in a fort or castle. Ninth, in a guardroom, police-station, or in any government place where prisoners are confined. Tenth, on a highway. Eleventh, in a house of another person. Twelfth, in the forest. Thirteenth, in an open place, such as a meadow or an upland. Fourteenth, on ground where men are buried or burned. The consequences of carnal connection at such places are always disastrous; they breed misfortunes, and, if children be begotten, these turn out bad and malicious persons.

The following are the times when women are not to be enjoyed:—First, by day, unless their class and temperament require coition during the light hours. Second, during or at the Sankránti-parvaní, that is to say, when the sun or a planet passes from one side of the zodiac to another.[1] Third, during the Sharad, or cold season[2]

1 Parvani (Sanskrit Parva), is applied to certain times, such as the solstices and the equinoxes, when good actions are most acceptable.

2 It must be remembered that during the whole period of the sun's southing (Dakshanáyana, opposed to Uttaráyana, or his northerly direction), the high-caste Hindu will not marry.

(October to November.) Fourth, during the Grishma, or hot season[1] (June to July). Fifth, in the Amávásyá (the last, the thirtieth, or the new moon day of the Hindu month), unless the Love-shástra specify the contrary. Sixth, during the periods when the man's body suffers from fever. Seventh, during the time of a "Vrata," any self-imposed religious observance, with obligation to carry it out. Eighth, in the evening time; and ninth, when wearied with wayfare. The consequences of congress at such epochs are as disastrous as if the act took place in a prohibited spot.

The following is the situation which the wise men of old have described as being best fitted for sexual intercourse with women. Choose the largest, and finest, and the most airy room in the house, purify it thoroughly with white-wash, and decorate its spacious and beautiful walls with pictures and other objects upon which the eye may dwell with delight.[2] Scattered about this apartment place musical instruments, especially the pipe and the lute; with refreshments, as cocoa-nut, betel-leaf and milk, which is so useful for retaining and restoring vigour; bottles of rose water and various essences, fans and chauris for

[1] The other four are Vasanta, or spring (April to May); Varshà, the rains (August to September); Hermanta, or the cold season (December to January); and Shishirá, early spring (February to March). Thus the Hindu year contains six Ritú or seasons.

[2] This precaution might be adopted in modern civilization. It was practised by the Greeks and Romans, for the purpose of be-getting graceful and beautiful children; and, considering the history of mother-marks and other puerperal curiosities, we should be careful how we determine that the conception cannot be favourably, as well as unfavourably influenced by the aspect of objects around the parents.

cooling the air, and books containing amorous songs, and gladdening the glance with illustrations of love-postures. Splendid Divàlgiri, or wall lights, should gleam around the hall, reflected by a hundred mirrors, whilst both man and woman should contend against any reserve, or false shame, giving themselves up in complete nakedness to unrestrained voluptuousness, upon a high and handsome bedstead, raised on tall legs, furnished with many pillows, and covered by a rich chatra, or canopy; the sheets being besprinkled with flowers and the coverlet scented by burning luscious incense, such as aloes and other fragrant woods.[1] In such a place, let the man, ascending the throne of love, enjoy the woman in ease and comfort, gratifying his and her every wish and every whim.

CHAPTER IX.

Treating of External Enjoyments.

By "external enjoyments" are meant the processes which should always precede internal enjoyment or coition. The wise have said that before congress, we must develope the desire of the weaker sex through certain perliminaries, which are many and various; such as the various embraces and kisses; the Nakhadána, or unguiculations; the

1 Concerning the effect of perfumes upon the organs, see Chap. IX.

Dashanas, or morsications; the Kesha-grahanas, or manipulating the hair, and other amorous blandishments. These affect the senses and divert the mind from coyness and coldness. After which tricks and toyings, the lover will proceed to take possession of the place.

There are eight A'linganas, or modes of embracing, which will here be enumerated and carefully described.[1]—

1. Vrikshádhirŭdha is the embrace which simulates the climbing of a tree,[2] and it is done as follows:—When the husband stands up the wife should place one foot upon his foot,[3] and raise the other leg to the height of his thigh, against which she presses it. Then encircling his waist with her arms, even as a man prepares to swarm up a palm-trunk, she holds and presses him forcibly, bends her body over his, and kisses him as if sucking the water of life.

2. Tila-Tandula, the embrace which represents the mixture of sesamum-seed with husked rice (Tandul). The man and woman, standing in front of each other, should

[1] The Alinganas are illustrated in almost every edition of "Koka Pandit," and so are the broader subjects treated of in the following chapter. At Puna (Poonah) and other parts of Western India, there are artists who make this the business of their lives, and who sell a series of about eighty body colours, at the rate of two to five Rupees each. The treatment is purely conventional, and the faces, as well as the dresses, probably date from several centuries ago. A change took place when an unhappy Anglo-Indian Officer, wishing to send home a portrait of his wife, applied to one of our artists with that admirably naive ignorance of everything "native," which is the growing custom of his race. The result was that the English-woman's golden hair and beautiful features appear in some fifty or sixty highly compromising attitudes, and will continue to do so for many a generation to come.

[2] Compare the slang word in French, "grimper."

[3] Both feet being, of course, naked.

fold each other to the bosom by closely encircling the waist. Then taking care to remain still, and by no means to move, they should approach the Linga to the Yoní, both being veiled by the dress, and avoid interrupting the contact for some time.

3. Lálátika, so called because forehead (láláta) touches forehead. In this position great endearment is shown by the close pressure of arms round the waist, both still standing upright, and by the contact of brow, cheek, and eyes, of mouth, breasts, and stomach.

4. Jághan-álingana, meaning "hips, loins, and thighs." In this embrace the husband sits[1] upon the carpet and the wife upon his thighs, embracing and kissing him with fond affection. In returning her fondling, her Lungaden, or petticoats, are raised, so that her Lungi, or undergarments, may come in contact with his clothes, and her hair is thrown into the dishevelled state symbolizing passion; or the husband, for variety's sake, may sit upon the wife's lap.

5. Viddhaka, when the nipples touch the opposite body. The husband sits still, closing his eyes, and the wife, placing herself close to him, should pass her right arm over his shoulder and apply her bosom to his, pressing him forcibly whilst he returns her embrace with equal warmth.

6. Urupagudha, so called from the use of the thighs. In this embrace both stand up, passing their arms round each other, and the husband places his wife's legs between

[1] Sitting invariably means cross-legged, like a tailor upon his board, or at squat, like a bird, and the seat is a mat, or carpet, in India, and a divan in the nearer East.

his own so that the inside of his thighs may come in contact with the outside of hers. As in all cases, kissing must be kept up from time to time. This is a process peculiar to those who are greatly enamoured of each other.

7. Dughdanír-álingana, or the "milk and water embrace," also called "Kshíraníra," with the same signification. In this mode the husband lies upon the bed, resting on one side, right or left; the wife throws herself down near him with her face to his, and closely embraces him, the members and limbs of both touching, and entangled, as it were, with the corresponding parts of the other. And thus they should remain until desire is thoroughly aroused in both.

8. Vallarí-vreshtita, or "embracing as the creeper twines about the tree," is performed as follows:—Whilst both are standing upright, the wife clings to her husband's waist, and passes her leg around his thigh, kissing him repeatedly and softly until he draws in his breath like one suffering from the cold. In fact, she must endeavour to imitate the vine enfolding the tree which supports it.

Here end the embracements; they should be closely studied, followed up by proper intelligence of the various modes of kisses, which must accompany and conclude the A'linganas. And understand at once that there are seven places highly proper for osculation, in fact, where all the world kisses. These are—First, the lower lip. Second, both the eyes. Third, both the cheeks. Fourth, the head.[1]

[1] In Europe, osculation upon the head and forehead is a paternal salutation, and, as a rule, men kiss one another upon both cheeks, and only their wives and concubines on the mouth. These distinctions are ignored by Orientals.

Fifth, the mouth. Sixth, both breasts; and seventh, the shoulders. It is true that the people of certain countries have other places, which they think proper to kiss; for instance, the voluptaries of Sáta-desha have adopted the following formula:—

But this is far from being customary with the men of our country or of the world in general.

Furthermore, there are ten different kinds of kisses, each of which has its own and proper name, and these will be described in due order.

1. Milita-kissing, which means "mishrita," mixing or reconciling. If the wife be angry, no matter however little, she will not kiss the face of her husband; the latter then should forcibly fix his lips upon hers and keep both mouths united till her ill-temper passes away.

2. Sphurita-kissing, which is connected with twitching and vellication. The wife should approach her mouth to that of her husband's, who then kisses her lower lip, whilst she draws it away, jerking, as it were, without any return of osculation.

3. Ghatika, or neck-nape kissing, a term frequently used by the poets. This is done by the wife, who, excited with passion, covers her husband's eyes with her hands, and closing her own eyes, thrusts her tongue into his mouth, moving it to and fro with a motion so pleasant and

slow that it at once suggests another and a higher form of enjoyment.

4. Tiryak, or oblique kissing. In this form the husband, standing behind or at the side of his wife, places his hand beneath her chin, catches hold of it and raises it, until he has made her face look up to the sky;[1] then he takes her lower lip beneath his teeth, gently biting and chewing it.

5. Uttaroshtha, or "upper-lip-kissing." When the wife is full of desire, she should take her husband's lower lip between her teeth, chewing and biting it gently; whilst he does the same to her upper lip. In this way both excite themselves to th height of passion.

6. Pindita, or "lump-kissing." The wife takes hold of her husband's lips with her fingers, passes her tongue over them and bites them.

7. Samputa, or "casket-kissing." In this form the husband kisses the inside mouth of his wife, whilst she does the same to him.

8. Hanuvatra-kissing.[2] In this mode the kiss should not be given at once, but begin with moving the lips towards one another in an irritating way, with freaks, pranks, and frolics. After toying together for some time, the mouths should be advanced, and the kiss exchanged.

9. Pratibodha, or "awakening kiss." When the hus-

---

[1] A fair specimen of the verbosity of Hindu style, which is so seldom realized or copied by Europeans speaking "native" languages. We should say "hold her chin and raise her face," or, to quote Ovid's Metamorphoses, "ad lumina lumen"—Attollens, which the Hindu would only half understand. This remark might be illustrated at considerable length.

[2] In Sanskrit, "Hanu" means jaw.

band, who has been absent for some time, returns home and finds his wife sleeping upon the carpet in a solitary bedroom, he fixes his lips upon hers, gradually increasing the pressure until such time as she awakes. This is by far the most agreeable form of osculation, and it leaves the most pleasant of memories.

10. Samaushtha-kissing. This is done by the wife taking her husband's mouth and lips into hers, pressing them with her tongue, and dancing about him as she does so.

Here end the sundry forms of kisses. And now must be described the various ways of Nakhadána, that is, of titillating and scratching with the nails. As it will not be understood what places are properest for this kind of dalliance, it should be explained as a preliminary that there are eleven parts upon which pressure may be exerted with more or less force. These are:—First, the neck. Second, the hands. Third, both thighs. Fourth, both breasts. Fifth, the back. Sixth, the sides. Seventh, both axillæ. Eighth, the whole chest or bosom. Ninth, both hips. Tenth, the Mons Veneris and all the parts about the Yoní; and, eleventh, both the cheeks.

Furthermore, it is necessary to learn the times and seasons when this style of manipulation is advisable. These are:—First, when there is anger in the mind of the woman. Second, at the time of first enjoying her or of taking her virginity. Third, when going to separate for a short time. Fourth, when about journeying to a foreign and distant country. Fifth, when a great pecuniary loss has been sustained. Sixth, when excited with desire of congress; and, seventh, at the season of Virati, that is to say, when there is no Ratí, or furor venereus.[1] At such times the nails should be applied to the proper places.

The nails, when in good condition and properest for use, are without spots[2] and lines, clean, bright, convex,[3] hard, and unbroken. Wise men have given in the Shastras these six qualities of the nails.

There are seven different ways of applying the nails, which may be remembered by the following Mandalaka or oblong formula:—

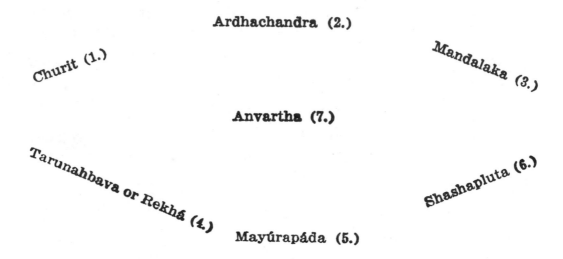

Ardhachandra (2.)

Churit (1.)

Mandalaka (3.)

Anvartha (7.)

Tarunahbava or Rekhá (4.)

Shashapluta (6.)

Mayúrapáda (5.)

---

[1] "Viratí" usually signifies being freed or refraining from carnal and worldly desires and passions; the extinction of earthly affections, and so forth.

[2] The Hindus do not appear to have any special superstition about the white spots on the nails, which the vulgar of Europe call "gifts," because they portend presents.

[3] Some wrongly translate this word "growing," or increasing. It means convex; in fact, what we call "filbert nails," opposed to the flat, the concave, and the spatulated.

1. Churit-nakhadána is setting the nails in such a way upon the cheeks, lower lip and breasts, without leaving any marks, but causing horripilation, till the woman's body-hair bristles up, and a shudder passes all over the limbs.[1]

2. Ardhachandra-nakhadána is effected by impressing with the nails upon the neck and breasts a curved mark, which resembles a half-moon (Ardha-chandra).

3. Mandalaka is applying the nails to the face for some time, and indeed until a sign is left upon it.

4. Tarunabhava or Rekhá (a line) is the name given by men conversant with the Kámashastra to nail-marks longer than two or three finger-breadths on the woman's head, thighs and breasts.

5. The Mayŭrapáda ("peacock's foot" or claw) is made by placing the thumb upon the nipple, and the four fingers upon the breast adjacent, at the same time pressing the nails till the mark resembles the trail of the peacock, which he leaves when walking upon mud.

.6 Shasha-pluta, or the "hopping of a hare," is the mark made upon the darker part of the breast when no other portion is affected.

7. Anvartha-nakhadána is a name applied to the three deep marks or scratches made by the nails of the first

---

1 The European superstition is, that when horripilation takes place without apparent cause, a person is passing over the spot where the shudderer will be buried. This idea can hardly exist amongst a people who sensibly burn their dead in fixed places, far removed from the haunts of the living; and amongst Muslims, as well as Hindus, the "goose flesh," as we call it in our homely way, is a sign of all the passions.

three fingers on the back, the breasts and the parts about the Yoní. This Nakhadána or unguiculation is highly proper when going abroad to a distant country, as it serves for a keepsake and a token of remembrance.

The voluptuary, by applying the nails as above directed with love and affection, and driven wild by the fury of passion, affords the greatest comfort to the sexual desires of the woman; in fact, there is nothing, perhaps, which is more delightful to both husband and wife than the skilful use of unguiculation.

Furthermore, it is advisable to master the proper mode of morsication or biting. It is said by persons who are absorbed in the study of sexual intercourse, that the teeth should be used to the same places where the nails are applied with the exception, however, of the eyes, the upper lip, and the tongue. Moreover, the teeth should be pressed until such time as the woman begins to exclaim, Hu! hu![1] after which enough has been done.

The teeth to be preferred in the husband, are those whose colour is somewhat rosy,[2] and not of a dead white; which are bright and clean, strong, pointed and short, and which form close and regular rows. On the other hand, those are bad which are dingy and unclean, narrow, long,

[1] This interjection usually denotes grief or pain, and here perhaps it is used in the latter sense.

[2] "Rosy teeth" suggest a resemblance to our "curly teeth," popularly associated with straight hair. The author, however, is right according to the most modern and the best authorities, in asserting that dead white is a bad colour, liable to caries, and easily tarnishing.

and projecting forward, as though they would leave the mouth.[1]

Like the unguiculations, there are seven different Dashanas or ways of applying the teeth, which may be remembered by the following Mandalaka or oblong formula:[2]

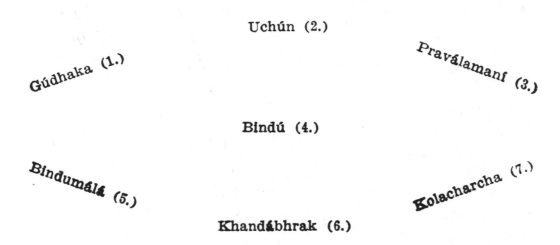

Uchún (2.)

Gúdhaka (1.)

Praválamaní (3.)

Bindú (4.)

Bindumálá (5.)

Kolacharcha (7.)

Khandábhrak (6.)

1. Gŭdhaka-dashana, or "secret-biting," is applying the teeth only to the inner or red part[3] of the woman's lip, leaving no outside mark so as to be seen by the world.

2. Uchŭn-dashana, the wise tell us, is the word applied to biting any part of a woman's lips or cheeks.

3. Praválamaní-dashana, or "coral-biting," is that wonderful union of the man's tooth and the woman's lips, which converts desire into a burning flame; it cannot be

1 Prognathism and Macrodontism are unknown to the higher castes of Hindus.

2 Also called Dashanágramandal or circle of the principle bitings.

3 The darker Hindus, like Africans, do not show redness in the lips, and the Arabs, curious to say, exceedingly admire brown lips.

described, and is to be accomplished only by long experience, not by the short practice of a few days.

4. Bindu-dashana ("dot" or "drop-biting") is the mark left by the husband's two front teeth upon the woman's lower lip, or upon the place where the Tillá or brow-mark is worn.

5. Bindu-málá, a "rosary," or "row of dots" or "drops," is the same as the preceding, except that all the front teeth are applied, so as to form a regular line of marks.

6. Khandábhrak is the cluster or multitude of impressions made by the prints of the husband's teeth upon the brow and cheek, the neck and breast of the wife. If disposed over the body like the Mandalaka, or Dashanágramandal, the mouth-shaped oblong traced above, it will add greatly to her beauty.

7. Kolacharcha is the name given by the wise to the deep and lasting marks of his teeth which the husband, in the heat of passion, and in the grief of departure when going to a foreign land, leaves upon the body of his wife. After his disappearance, she will look at them, and will frequently remember him with yearning heart.

So far for the styles of morsication. And now it is advisable to study the different fashions of Keshagrahana, or manipulating the hair, which, upon a woman's head, should be soft, close, thick, black, and wavy, nor curled, nor straight.

One of the best ways of kindling hot desire in a woman is, at the time of rising, softly to hold and handle the hair, according to the manner of doing so laid down in the Kámashastra.

The Keshagrahana are of four kinds, which may be remembered by the

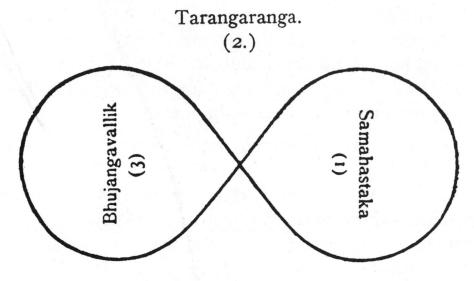

Tarangaranga.
(2.)

Kámávavatansa.
(4.)

1. Samahastakakeshagrahana, or "holding the hair with both hands," is when the husband encloses it between his two palms behind his wife's head, at the same time kissing her lower lip.

2. Tarangarangakeshagrahana, or "kissing the hair in wavy (or sinuous) fashion," is when the husband draws his wife towards him by the back hair, and kisses her at the same time.

3. Bhujangavallika, or the "dragon's turn," [1] is when the husband, excited by the approaching prospect of sexual congress amorously seizes the hind knot of his wife's hair, at the same time closely embracing her. This is done

[1] Bhujanga is a dragon, a cobra, a snake generically, or a man who keeps a mistress.

in a standing position, and the legs should be crossed with one another. It is one of the most exciting of all toyings.

4. Kámávatansakeshagrahana, or "holding the crest-hair of love," [1] is when, during the act of copulation, the husband holds with both hands his wife's hair above her ears, whilst she does the same thing to him, and both exchange frequent kisses upon the mouth.

Such, then, are the external enjoyments described in the due order according to which they ought to be practised. Those only are mentioned which are well known to, and are highly appreciated by the world. There are many others by no means so popular, and these are omitted, lest this treatise become an unwieldly size.[2] The following may, however, be mentioned:—

The blandishments of love are a manner of battle, in which the stronger wins the day. And in order to assist

[1] Avatansa means a crest, a tuft, or an earring.

[2] The reader will remember that the Hindus, as a rule, are a race of vegetarians, who rarely drink any stimulant such as wine, ale and spirits, or even tea, coffee and chocolate. They look with horror upon the meat-eater, that makes his body a grave for the corpses of animals; and they attach a bad name to all narcotics except tobacco, leaving opium and Bhang or Hashísh to low fellows and ribald debauchees. It is evident that, under such circumstances, their desires, after the first heat of youth, will be comparatively cold, and that both sexes, especially the weaker, require to be excited by a multitude and a variety of preliminaries to possession, which would defeat their own object in case of Europeans. Thus also we may account for their faith in pepper, ginger, cloves, cinnamon, and other spices which go by the name of "Garm Masálà," or hot condiments; these would have scanty effect upon the beef-eating and beer-bibbling Briton, but they exert a sufficiently powerful action upon a people of water-drinkers and rice or pulse-feeders.

us in the struggle, there are two forms of attack, known as Karatádana and Sitkreutoddesha.

Karatádana, as the word denotes,[1] are soft tappings and pattings with the hand, by the husband or the wife, upon certain members of each other's persons. And in this process there are four divisions, which the man applies to the woman:—

1. Prasritahasta, or patting with the open palm.

2. Uttányahasta, the same reversed; done with the back of the hand.

3. Mushti, or striking gently with the lower or fleshy part of the closed hand; softly hammering, as it were.

4. Sampátahasta, or patting with the inner part of the hand, which is slightly hollowed for the purpose, like the cobra's hood.

And here may be specified the several members that should thus be operated upon. First, the flesh below the ribs, with No. 1. Second the Mons Veneris and vicinity of the Yoní; also with No. 1. Third, the bosom and breasts, with No. 2. Fourth, the back and hip, with No. 3. Fifth, the head with No. 4.

There are also four corresponding divisions of the practices used by the woman to the man:—

1. Santánika, a name given by learned men to the act of a wife gently patting with the closed fist her husband's breast, when the two have become one, so as to increase his pleasure.

2. Patáká is when the wife, also during congress, pats her husband gently with the open hand.

1 "Kara," a hand, and Tádana, "striking."

3. Bindumálá is the name given only by men when the wife, at the time of coition, fillips her husband's body with the thumbs only.

4. Kundalá is the name given by the older poets when the wife, during copulation, fillips her husband's body with thumb and fore-finger, not with the rest of the hand.

And now of the Sítkrití, or inarticulate sound produced by drawing in the breath between the closed teeth; these are the peculiar privilege and prerogative of women, and the wise divide them into five kinds:—

1. Hinkrití is the deep and grave sound, like "Hun! hun! hun!" "Hin! hin! hin!" [1] produced in the nose and mouth with the slightest use of the former member.

2. Stanita is the low rumbling, like distant thunder, expressed by "Ha! ha!" or by "Hán! hán! hán!" produced by the throat without the concurrence of the nasal muscles.

3. Sítkrití is the expiration or emission of breath, like the hissing of a serpent, expressed by "Shan! shan!" or "Shish! shish!" and produced only in the mouth.

4. Utkriti is the crackling sound, resembling the splitting of a bamboo, expressed by "T'hat! t'hat!" and formed by applying the tongue-tip to the palate, [2] and by moving it as rapidly as possible, at the same time pronouncing the interjection.

5. Bhavakriti is a rattling sound, like the fall of heavy rain-drops, expressed by "T'hap! t'hap!" produced by

[1] In all these interjections, the terminal liquid is a highly nasalized nunnation.

[2] Somewhat in the same way as an Englishman urges on a horse.

the lips; but it can be produced only at the time of congress.

These several Sítkritís in the woman's mouth at the moment of enjoyment, will respectively resemble the cry of the quail (Láva), of the Indian cuckoo (Kokila), of the spotted-necked pigeon (Kapota), of the Hansa-goose and of the peacock. The sounds should especially be produced when the husband kisses, bites, and chews his wife's lower lip; and the sweetness of the uterance greatly adds to enjoyment, and promotes the congress of the sexual act.

Furthermore, be it known to men the peculiar characteristics of the Ashtamahánáyika, or the eight great forms of Nayiká :[1]—

1. Khanditanáyiká, when the husband bears upon his body all the marks of sexual enjoyment, produced by sleeping with a rival wife; and when, with eyes reddened by keeping late hours, he returns to his beloved struck with fear and in an agitated state, coaxing her, and speaking sweet words, for the purpose of sueing her to congress, and she half listens to him, but yields at last. Such is the name given to her by the great poets of the olden time.

2. Vásakasajjitá is the word applied by the learned to the wife, who, having spread a soft, fine bed, in a charming apartment, sits upon it at night-time, and awaits her husband, with great expectation, now half closing her eyes, then fixing her glance on the door.

---

[1] A mistress, or one beloved, the feminine of Náyak, meaning the head, a chief, the lover, the hero of a play, or the best gem in a necklace; hence the corrupted word "Naik," a corporal in the "native" army.

3. Kalakántaritá, say the wise men, is the term for a wife, who when her husband, after grossly injuring her, falls at her feet and begs for pardon, answers loudly and in great wrath, drives him from her presence, and determines not to see him again; but presently, waxing repentant, laments in various ways the pains and sorrows of separation, and at last recovers quietude by the hope of reunion.

4. Abhisáriká is the woman whose sexual passions being in a state of overflowing, dresses herself, and goes forth shamelessly, and wantonly at night-time to the house of some strange man, in the hope of carnal copulation with him.

5. Vipralabdhá is the disappointed woman, who, having sent a go-between to some strange man, appointing him to meet her at a certain place, repairs there, confused and agitated with the prospect of congress, but sees the go-between returning alone, and without the lover, which throws her into a state of fever.

.6 Viyogini is the melancholy woman, who, during the absence of her husband in a far country, smells the fragrant and exciting perfumes[1] of sandal-wood, and other odorous substances, and looking upon the lotus-flower and the moonlight, falls into a passion of grief.

7. Svádhinapúrvapatiká is the name given to the wife

---

[1] There are many theories upon this subject in the East. For instance, the Narcissus-flower is everywhere supposed to excite the woman and depress the man, whilst the Mimosa blossom gives an essence which the Arabs call "Fitnah," trouble or revolt, because its action is direct and powerful upon the passions of their wives as the Spanish "Viento de las mujeres."

whose husband instead of gratifying her amorous desires, and studying her carnal wants, engages in the pursuit of philosophic knowledge derived from meditation.

8. Utkanthitá, according to the best poets, is the woman who loves her husband very dearly, whose eyes are light and lively, who has decorated herself with jewels and garlands, well knowing the wishes of her man, and who, burning with desire, awaits his coming, propped up with pillows in a sleeping-apartment appropriated to pleasure, and sumptuously adorned with mirrors and pictures.[1]

CHAPTER X.

Treating of internal enjoyments in its various forms.

———

By "internal enjoyment" is meant the art of congress which follows the various external preliminaries described in the last chapter. These embraces, kisses and sundry manipulations, must always be practised according to the taste of husband and wife, and if persisted in as the Shastra directs, they will excessively excite the passions of the woman, and will soften and loosen her Yoní so as to be ready for carnal connection.

1 These eight Náyikás are borrowed from the language of the Hindu drama.

The following verses show how much art and science there is in a matter which appears so simple to the uneducated and vulgar.

"What is the remedy when a woman is mightier than a man? Although she be very strong, yet no sooner are her legs placed wide apart, than she loses her force of passion, and is satisfied."

"Thus the Yoní from being tight and compact, becomes slack and loose; let the husband, therefore, press her thighs together, and she will be equally able to struggle with him at the time of congress."

"Well, if a woman be only twelve or thirteen years old, and the man is quite grown up, and has lost the first vigour of his youth, what must be done to make them equal?"

"In such a case, the legs of the woman must be stretched out to the fullest extent, so as to weaken the powers, and by these means the man will prove himself her equal."

There are five main Bandha or A'sana—forms or postures of congress—which appear in the following shape,

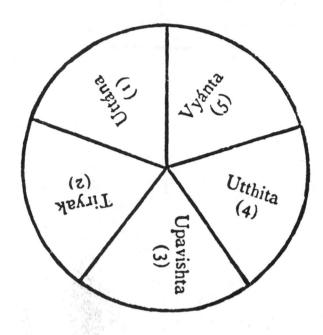

and each of these will require its own description successively, and in due order.[1]

[1] The reader will bear in mind that the exceeding pliability of the Hindu's limbs enables him to assume attitudes absolutely impossible to the Europeans, and his chief object in congress is to avoid tension of the muscles, which would shorten the period of enjoyment. For which reason, even in the act of love, he will delay to talk, to caress his wife, to eat, drink, chew Pán-supári, and perhaps smoke a water-pipe.

Stripped of its excessive verbiage, the Hindu "façons de faire," are simple enough. The five great divisions represent: 1. The woman lying supine (upon her back); 2. Lying on her side (right or left); 3. Sitting in various ways; 4. Standing, or as the vulgar call, an upright; and, lastly, 5. Lying prone (upon breast and stomach). Of the first division, there are eleven subdivisions; of the second, three; of the third, ten; of the fourth, three; and two

(A) Uttána-bandha (*i. e.*, supine posture) is the great division so-called by men well versed in the art of Love, when a woman lies upon her back, and her husband sits close to her upon his hams. But is this all that can be said of it? No! no! there are eleven subdivisions, as shown in the following table:—

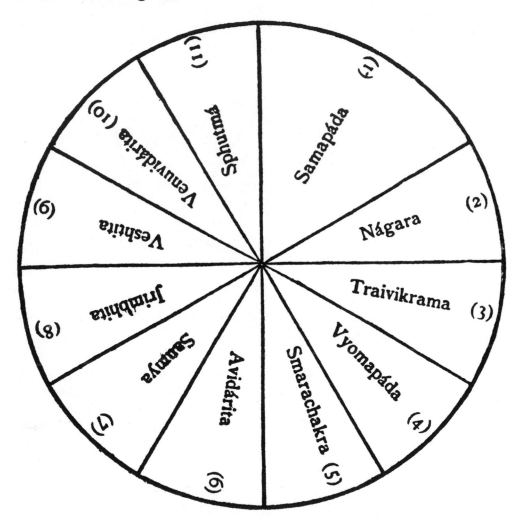

of the fifth class, making a total of twenty-nine, and with three forms of Purúháyit, a grand total of thirty-two.

As in similar European treatises, the Kámashartra is very brief and unsatisfactory, except in the principal positions, and it can

And now of the several sub-divisions:—

1. Samapáda-ŭttána-bandha, is when the husband places his wife upon her back, raises both her legs, and placing them upon his shoulders, sits close to her and enjoys her.

2. Nágara-ŭttána-bandha, is when the husband places his wife upon her back, sits between her legs, raises them both, keeping them on the other side of his waist, and thus enjoys her.

3. Traivikrama-ŭttána-bandha, is when one of the wife's legs is left lying upon the bed or carpet, the other being placed upon the head of the husband, who supports himself upon both hands. This position is very admirable.

4. Vyomapáda-ŭttána-bandha, is when the wife, lying upon her back, raises with her hands both legs, drawing them as far back as her hair; the husband, then sitting close to her, places both hands upon her breasts and enjoys her.

5. Smarachakrásana, or the position of the Káma's wheel, a mode very much enjoyed by the voluptuary. In

hardly be understood without illustrations. Some appear to be identical with others, at least no distinction can be learnt from the text. Moreover, it is evident that the Yoni of the Hindu woman must be placed exceptionally high, otherwise many of the postures would be quite impossible—these varieties of conformation are exceedingly interesting to the ethnologist, but the matter is far too extensive for discussing here. The subject of constricting the Yoni is also ethnologically of great importance, as will be seen when the reader arrives at the paragraph. An allusion has already been made to the Hindu practice of affecting conception by both parents looking at pictures of noble and beautiful forms; a custom well-known to the ancients, but now unaccountably neglected. (See Chap. VIII).

this form, the husband sits between the legs of his wife, extends his arms on both sides of her as far as he can, and thus enjoys her.

6. Avidárita is that position when the wife raises both her legs, so that they may touch the bosom of her husband, who, sitting between her thighs, embraces and enjoys her.

7. Saumya-bandha is the name given by the old poets to a form of congress much in vogue amongst the artful students of the Kámashastra. The wife lies supine, and the husband, as usual, sits;[1] he places both hands under her back, closely embracing her, which she returns by tightly grasping his neck.

8. Jrimbhita-ásana. In order to bend the wife's body in the form of a bow, the husband places little pillows or pads beneath her hips and head, he then raises the seat of pleasure and rises to it by kneeling upon a cushion. This is an admirable form of congress, and is greatly enjoyed by both.

9. Veshtita-ásana, is when the wife lies upon her back cross legged,[2] and raises her feet a little; this position is very well fitted for those burning with desire.

10. Venuvidárita is that in which the wife, lying upon her back, places one leg upon her husband's shoulder, and the other on the bed or carpet.

11. Sphutmá-ŭttána-bandha is when the husband, after insertion and penetration, raises the legs of his wife, who

[1] Not as a tailor, but "sitting at squat," upon both feet, somewhat like a bird, a position impossible to Europeans.

[2] Unintelligible without an illustration.

still lies upon her back, and joins her thighs closely together.

Here end the eleven forms of Uttána-bandha; we now proceed to the:—

(B) Tiryak (*i. e.*, aslant, awry posture) whose essence consists of the woman lying upon her side. Of this division, there are three sub-divisions:—

1. Vínaka-tiryak-bandha is when the husband, placing himself alongside of his wife, raises one of his legs over his hip and leaves the other lying upon the bed or carpet. This A'sana (position) is fitted only for practice upon a grown-up woman; in the case of a younger person, the result is by no means satisfactory.

2. Samputa-tiryak-bandha is when both man and woman lie straight upon their sides, without any movement or change in the position of their limbs.

3. Karkata-tiryak-bandha is when both being upon their sides, the husband lies between his wife's thighs, one under him, and the other being thrown over his flank, a little below the breast.

Here end the three forms of the Tiryak-bandha; and, we now proceed to the:—

(C) Upavishta (*i. e.*, sitting) posture. Of this division there are ten sub-divisions shown in the following figure:

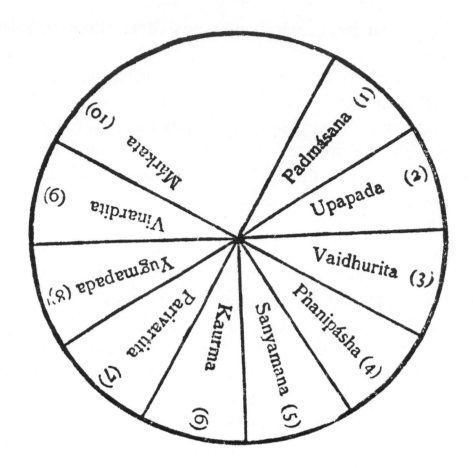

1. Padm-ásana.   The husband in this favourite position sits crossed-legged upon the bed or carpet, and takes his wife upon his lap, placing his hands upon her shoulders.

2. Upapad-ásana.   In this posture, whilst both are sitting, the woman slightly raises one leg by placing the hand under it, and the husband enjoys her.

3. Vaidhurit-ásana.   The husband embraces his wife's neck very closely, and she does the same to him.

4. Phanipásh-ásana. The husband holds his wife's feet, and the wife those of her husband.

5. Sanyaman-ásana.   The husband passes both legs of

his wife under his arms at the elbow, and holds her neck with his hands.

6. Kaurmak-ásana (or the tortoise posture). The husband must so sit that his mouth, arms, and legs, touch the corresponding members of his wife.

7. Parivartit-ásana. In addition to the mutual contact of mouth, arms, and legs, the husband must frequently pass both the legs of his wife under his arms at the elbow.

8. Yugmapad-ásana is a name given by the best poets to that position in which the husband sits with his legs wide apart, and, after insertion and penetration, presses the thighs of his wife together.

9. Vinarditásana, a form possible only to a very strong man with a very light woman, he raises her by passing both her legs over his arms at the elbow, and moves her about from left to right, but not backwards or forwards, till the supreme moment arrives.

10. Márkatásana, is the same position as No. 9; in this, however, the husband moves the wife in a straight line away from his face, that is, backwards and forwards, but not from side to side.

Here end the forms of Upavishta, or sitting- posture. The next is :—

(D) Utthita, or the standing posture, which admits of three sub-divisions :—

1. Jánu-kŭru-utthitha-bandha (that is, "knee and elbow standing-form,") a posture which also requires great bodily strength in the man. Both stand opposite to each other, and the husband passes his two arms under his wife's knees, supporting her upon the *saignée,* or inner

elbow; he then raises her as high as his waist, and enjoys her, whilst she must clasp his neck with both her hands.

2. Hari-vikrama-utthita-bandha: in this form the husband raises only one leg of his wife, who with the other stands upon the ground. It is a position delightful to young women, who thereby soon find themselves *in gloriâ*.

3. Kírti-utthita-bandha: this requires strength in the man, but not so much as is wanted for the first subdivision. The wife, clasping her hands and placing her legs round her husband's waist, hangs, as it were, to him, whilst he supports her by placing his fore-arms under her hips.

Here end the forms of Utthita, or standing-posture; and we now come to the:—

(E) Vyánta-bandha, which means congress with a woman when she is prone, that is, with the breast and stomach to the bed or carpet. Of this A'sana, there are only two well-known sub-divisions:—

1. Dhenuka-vyânta-bandha (the cow-posture[1]): in this position the wife places herself upon all fours, supported on her hands and feet (not her knees), and the husband, approaching from behind, falls upon her waist, and enjoys her as if he were a bull. There is much religious merit in this form.

2. Aybha-vyánta-bandha (or Gajásawa, the elephant posture[2]). The wife lies down in such a position that her

[1] There is nothing of insult in comparison with a cow, which is worshipped by the Hindus.

[2] The classical idea of elephants, like other retromingents, copulating "à tergo," was never known to the Hindus, who were too well acquainted with the habits of the animals. It is needless to say that their coition is that of other quadrupeds.

face, breast, stomach, and thighs all touch the bed or carpet, and the husband, extending himself upon her, and bending himself like an elephant, with the small of the back much drawn in, works underneath her, and effects insertion.

"O Rajah," said the arch-poet Kalyâna-Malla, "there are many other forms of congress, such as Harinásana, Sŭkrásana, Gardhabásana, and so forth; but they are not known to the people, and being useless as well as very difficult of performance, nay, sometimes so full of faults as to be excluded or prohibited, I have, therefore, not related them to you. But if you desire to hear anything more about postures, be pleased to ask, and your servant will attempt to satisfy your curiosity."

"Right well!" exclaimed the king. "I much wish to hear you describe the Purŭsháyitabandha."

"Hear, O Rajah," resumed the poet, "whilst I relate all that requires to be known concerning that form of congress."

Purŭsháyitabandha[1] is the reverse of what men usually practise. In this case the man lies upon his back, draws his wife upon him and enjoys her. It is especially useful when he, being exhausted, is no longer capable of muscular exertion, and when she is ungratified, being still full of the water of love. The wife must, therefore, place her husband supine upon the bed or carpet, mount upon his person, and satisfy her desires. Of this form of congress there are three sub-divisions:—

[1] This position is held in great horror by Muslims, who commonly say, "Cursed be he who makes himself earth and woman heaven!"

1. Viparíta-bandha, or "contrary postition," is when the wife lies straight upon the outstretched person of her husband, her breast being applied to his bosom, presses his waist with her hands, and moving her hips sharply in various directions, enjoys him.

2. Purŭsháyita-bhramara-bandha ("like the large bee") : in this, the wife, having placed her husband at full length upon the bed or carpet, sits at squat upon his thighs, closes her legs firmly after she has effected insertion; and, moving her waist in a circular form, churning, as it were, enjoys her husband, and thoroughly satisfies herself.

3. Utthita-uttána-bandha. The wife, whose passion has not been gratified by previous copulation, should make her husband lie upon his back, and sitting cross-legged upon his thighs, should seize his Linga, effect insertion, and move her waist up and down, advancing and retiring; she will derive great comfort from this process.

Whilst thus reversing the natural order in all these forms of Purŭsháyita, the wife will draw in her breath after the fashion called Sitkâra; she will smile gently, and she will show a kind of half shame, making her face so attractive that it cannot well be described. After which she will say to her husband, "O my dear! O thou rogue; this day thou hast come under my control, and hast become subjected to me, being totally defeated in the battle of love!" Her husband manipulates her hair according to art, embraces her and kisses her lower lip; whereupon all her members will relax, she will close her eyes and fall into a swoon of joy.

Moreover, at all times of enjoying Purŭsháyita the wife will remember that without an especial exertion of will on her part, the husband's pleasure will not be perfect. To this end she must ever strive to close and constrict the Yoní until it holds the Linga, as, with a finger,[1] opening and shutting at her pleasure, and finally, acting as the hand of the Gopâla-girl, who milks the cow. This can be learned only by long practice, and especially by throwing the will into the part to be affected, even as men endeavour to sharpen their hearing,[2] and their sense of touch. While so doing, she will mentally repeat" Kámadeva! Kámadeva," in order that a blessing may rest upon the undertaking. And she will be pleased to hear that the act once learned, is never lost. Her husband will then value her above all women, nor would he exchange her for the most beautiful Pâní (queen) in the three worlds. So lovely and pleasant to man is she who constricts.

Let it now be observed that there are sundry kinds and conditions of women whom the wise peremptorily exclude

[1] Amongst some races the constrictor vaginæ muscles are abnormally developed. In Abyssinia, for instance, a woman can so exert them as to cause pain to a man, and, when sitting upon his thighs, she can induce the orgasm without moving any other part of her person. Such an artist is called by the Arabs, "Kabbázah," literally meaning "a holder," and it is not surprising that the slave dealers pay large sums for her. All women have more or less the power, but they wholly neglect it; indeed, there are many races in Europe which have never even heard of it. To these the words of wisdom spoken by Kalyána-Malla, the poet, should be peculiarly acceptable.

[2] So, it is said, that Orsini, the conspirator, employed the long hours of his captivity in cultivating this sense, until he was able readily to distinguish sounds which other men could not even hear.

[3] The author, at this place, repeats the signs and symptoms of plenary enjoyment in women which he gave in Chap. III., Sec. 3.

from Purŭsháyita, and the principal exceptions will here be mentioned. First, the Kariní-woman. Second, the Hariní. Third, she who is pregnant. Fourth, she who has not long left the lying-in chamber. Fifth, a woman of thin and lean body, because the exertion will be too great for her strength. Sixth, a woman suffering from fever or other weakening complaint. Seventh, a virgin; and, eighth, a girl not yet arrived at puberty.

And now having duly concluded the chapter of internal enjoyments, it is good to know that if husband and wife live together in close agreement, as one soul in a single body, they shall be happy in this world, and in that to come. Their good and charitable actions will be an example to mankind, and their peace and harmony will effect their salvation. No one yet has written a book to prevent the separation of the married pair and to show them how they may pass through life in union. Seeing this, I felt compassion, and composed the treatise, offering it to the god Pandurang.

The chief reason for the separation between the married couple and the cause, which drives the husband to the embraces of strange women, and the wife to the arms of strange men, is the want of varied pleasures and the monotony which follows possession. There is no doubt about it. Monotony begets satiety, and satiety distaste for congress, especially in one or the other; malicious feelings are engendered, the husband or the wife yield to temptation, and the other follows, being driven by jealousy. For it seldom happens that the two love each other equally, and in exact proportion, therefore is the one more easily seduced by passion than the other. From such separations result polygamy, adulteries, abortions, and every manner of vice, and not only do the erring husband and wife fall into the pit, but they also drag down the names of their deceased ancestors from the place of beautified mortals, either to hell or back again upon this world. Fully understanding the way in which such quarrels arise, I have in this book shown how the husband, by varying the enjoyment of his wife, may live with her as with thirty-two different women, ever varying the enjoyment of her, and rendering satiety impossible. I have also taught all manner of useful arts and mysteries, by which she may render herself pure, beautiful and pleasing in his eyes. Let me, therefore, conclude with the verse of blessing :—

"May this treatise, "Ananga-ranga," be beloved of man and woman, as long as the Holy River Ganges springeth from Shiva, with his wife Gauri on his left side; as long as Lakshmí loveth Vishnŭ; as long as Bramhá is engaged in the study of the Vedas; and as long as the earth, the moon and the sun endure."

FINIS.

APPENDIX I.[1]

ASTROLOGY IN CONNECTION WITH MARRIAGE.

Now is related the effect resulting from the consonance and dissonance, amity and hospitality, between the stars (and destinies) of a couple proposed to be bride and bridegroom.[2] Having ascertained that the houses (*kula*), the family names (*gotra*), and the individual dispositions (*svabháva*), of the postulants are free from inherent blemish,[3] their Gunas (qualities or requisites) must be determined from the zodiacal signs and the asterisms presiding over their birth.[4]

The Gunas, number in total thirty-six, of which at least nineteen are requisite for a prosperous match; and thence upwards, the fruit resulting from their influence is proportioned to their number.

1 We have relegated the astrological and chemical chapters to an appendix. They appear (pp. 120 et seq.) in the Maratha Edit. of the Ananga-Ranga (Bombay, 1842); but it is more than doubtful if they belong to the original work.

2 As mere children are married in India these precautions and considerations must be taken by the relatives. See the beginning of chapter VIII.

3 The fault of families is hereditary ill-repute: the greatest blemish of names is when those of bride and bridegroom exactly correspond, and those of disposition are too well known to require notice.

4 The signs and asterisms are set down in the horoscopes, which are drawn up at the child's birth by competent inquirers.

Observations upon these subjects will be facilitated by
the three following tables :—

Table I. shows the presiding planet, the genus (or
nature) and the caste (in theory not in practice) of the
questioner, when the zodiacal sign of his birth-time is
known. For instance, if Sol be in Aries at the birth of
the patient, his planet is Mars; he belongs to the genus
quadruped, and he is by caste a Kshatriya or fighting-man.

TABLE I.

Zodiacal Sign.	Presiding Planet	Genus	Caste
Aries	Mars	Quadruped	Kshatriya
Taurus	Venus	Quadruped	Vaishya
Gemini	Mercury	Human	Shudra
Cancer	Moon	Insect	Brahman
Leo	Sun	Quadruped	Kshatriya
Virgo	Mercury	Human	Vaishya
Libra	Venus	Human	Shudra
Scorpio	Mars	Insect	Brahman
Sagittarius	Jupiter	Man-horse	Kshatriya
Capricornus	Saturn	Water-man	Vaishya
Aquarius	Saturn	Human	Shudra
Pisces	Jupiter	Aquatic animal	Brahman

Table II. shows the number of Guna, or qualities,
requisite for a prosperous match distributed under eight
heads :—

TABLE II.

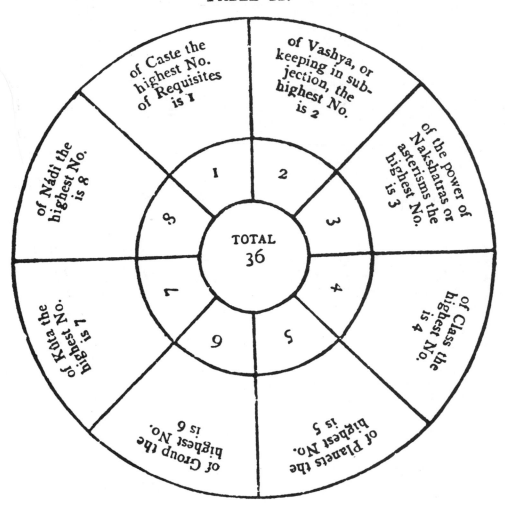

Table III. shows the group and class to which a person belongs when the asterism (Nakshatra, or lunar mansion) of his birth-time is known, together with his Nádi, or hour of twenty-four minutes. The twenty-seven asterisms are classed under three heads; of gods, of men and of demons (Rakshasas), and the asterism determines to which the querent belongs. Moreover, each asterism is divided in four quarters, and of these nine make one zodiacal sign. The name-letter used in that quarter stands for that quarter.

TABLE III.

Asterism (Nakshatra).	Group.	Class.	Nadi. Hour of 24 m.	Quarters of Asterisms, showing changes of the Zodiacal signs.			
				1	2	3	4
Ashvinî	God	Horse	First	Cha, 1, i. e. Aries	Che, 1, i. e. do.	Cho, 1, i. e. do.	Lâ, 1, i. e. do.
Bharani	Man	Elephant	Middle	Li, 1, i. e. do.	Lu, 1, i. e. do.	Le, 1, i. e. do.	Lo, 1, i. e. do.
Krittika	Demon	Ram	Last	A, 1, i. e. do.	I, 2, i. e. Taurus	U', 2, i. e. do.	Ve, 2, i. e. do.
Rohini	Man	Serpent	Last	O, 2, i. e. do.	Vâ, 2, i. e. do.	Vi, 2, i. e. do.	Vu, 2, i. e. do.
Mriga	God	Serpent	Middle	Ve, 2, i. e. do.	Vo, 2, i. e. do.	Kâ, 3, i. e. Gemini	Ki, 3, i. e. do.
Ardrâ	Man	Dog	First	Ku, 3, i. e. do.	Gha, 3, i. e. do.	Na, 3, i. e. do.	Chha, 3, i. e. do.
Punarvasu	God	Cat	First	Ke, 3, i. e. do.	Ko, 3, i. e. do.	Ha, 3, i. e. do.	Hi, 4, i. e. Cancer
Pushya	God	Ram	Middle	Hu, 4, i. e. do.	He, 4, i. e. do.	Ho, 4, i. e. do.	Da, 4, i. e. do.
A'shleshâ	Demon	Cat	Last	Di, 4, i. e. do.	Du, 4, i. e. do.	De, 4, i. e. do.	Do, 4, i. e. do.
Maghâ	Demon	Mouse	Last	Ma, 5, i. e. Leo	Mi, 5, i. e. do.	Mu, 5, i. e. do.	Me, 5, i. e. do.
Purvâ	Man	Mouse	Middle	Mo, 5, i. e. do.	Tâ, 5, i. e. do.	Ti, 5, i. e. do.	Tu, 5, i. e. do.
Uttarâ	Man	Cow	First	Te, 5, i. e. do.	To, 6, i. e. Virgo	Pa, 6, i. e. do.	Pi, 6, i. e. do.
Hasta	God	Buffalo	First	Pu, 6, i. e. do.	Shâ, 6, i. e. do.	Nâ, 6, i. e. do.	Dhâ, 1. e. do.

Table III.—continued.

Asterism (Nakshatra).	Group.	Class.	Nadi. Hour of 24 m.	Quarters of Asterisms, showing changes of the Zodiacal signs.			
				1	2	3	4
Chitrá	Demon	Tiger	Middle	Pe, 6, i. e. do.	Po, 6, i. e. do.	Rá, 7, i. e. Libra	Rí, 7, i. e. do.
Svátí	God	Buffalo	Last	Ru, 7, i. e. do.	Re, 7, i. e. do.	Ro, 7, i. e. do.	Lá, 7, i. e. do.
Vishákhá	Demon	Tiger	Last	Zi, 7, i. e. do.	Zu, 7, i. e. do.	Ze, 7, i. e. do.	Zo, 8, i. e. Scorpio
Anurádhá	God	Deer	Middle	Ná, 8, i. e. do.	Ni, 8, i. e. do.	Nu, 8, i. e. do.	Ne, 8, i. e. do.
Jyeshthá	Demon	Deer	First	No, 8, i. e. do.	Yá, 8, i. e. do.	Yí, 8, i. e. do.	Yu, 8, i. e. do.
Múla	Demon	Dog	First	Ye, 9, i. e. Sagittarius	Yo, 9, i. e. do.	Bhá, 9, i. e. do.	Bhí, 9, i. e. do.
Purváshádhá	Man	Monkey	Middle	Bhu, 9, i. e. do.	Dha, 9, i. e. do.	Phá, 9, i. e. do.	Dhá, 9, i. e. do.
Uttaráshádhá	Man	Ichneumon	Last	Bhe, 9, i. e. do.	Bho, 10, i. e. Capricornus	Ga, 10, i. e. do.	Gí, 10, i. e. do.
Shravana	God	Monkey	Last	Khí, 10, i. e. do.	Khu, 10, i. e. do.	Khe, 10, i. e. do.	Kho, 10, i. e. do.
Dhanishthá	Demon	Lion	Middle	Gá, 10, i. e. do.	Gi, 10, i. e. do.	Gu, 11, i. e. Aquarius	Ge, 11, i. e. do.
Shatatáraká	Demon	Horse	First	Go, 11, i. e. do.	Sá, 11, i. e. do.	Si, 11, i. e. do.	Su, 11, i. e. do.
Purvábhádrapada	Man	Lion	First	Se, 11, i. e. do.	So, 11, i. e. do.	Dá, 11, i. e. do.	Dí, 12, i. e. Pisces
Uttarábhádrapadá	Man	Cow	Middle	Du, 12, i. e. do.	Zam, 12, i. e. do.	N, 12, i. e. do.	Yo, 12, i. e. do.
Retatí	God	Elephant	Last	Do, 12, i. e. do.	Do, 12, i. e. do.	Chá, 12, i. e. do.	Chi, 12, i. e. do.

And now to consider the tables more carefully. As is shown by No. II. the Gunas are of various values, and are distributed under eight heads.

1. Caste. If both be of the same, or the caste of the bridegroom be higher, there is one Guna (of the thirty-six) otherwise there is none.

2. Vashya, or keeping in subjection, one of the prime considerations of marriage. If the zodiacal signs of the bride and bridegroom be of the same genus (Table I.) this represents two Gunas. If the person kept in subjection be also the "food" of the other, this counts for only one-half (Guna). If there be natural friendship between the genera of the bride and bridegroom this stands for two Gunas; and if one be an enemy to the other, and also keep the other in subjection, it represents only one Guna. The consideration is as follows:—To the human genus every quadruped, saving only the lion, remains in supbjection; for instance, the quadruped ram is subject to, and is the "food" of the human genus, with no exception except the Brahman. The same is the case with the fish and the crab amongst lower animals. The scorpion is the general enemy to the human race, and other animals are enemies as well as food. Thus we discover which of the two persons will hold the other in subjection.

3. The Nakshatras (Table III.) must be considered as follows:—The bride's asterism should be counted from that of the bridegroom, and the number be divided by nine. If the remainder be three, five or seven, it is a sign of bad fortune; and *vice versâ* with all others. Similarly the bridegroom's lunation should be counted from the bride's;

and if, after dividing as before by nine, the remainders of both parties indicate good fortune, this counts as three Gunas, the maximum. Only if one portend well, it counts as one Guna and a-half: otherwise there is no Guna.

4. Class. Perfect friendship counts for four Gunas; common friendship as three, indifference as two; enmity as one, an exceeding enmity as half a Guna. Perfect friendship can subsist only between two human beings of the same caste. Cows and buffalos, elephants and rams, live in common friendship. Cows and tigers, horses and buffalos, lions and elephants, rams and monkeys, dogs and deer, cats and mice, snakes and ichneumons are exceedingly inimical. Common enmity and indifference are easily exemplified by the lives or ordinary men and beasts.

5. Planets. If the presiding planets of both persons be the same, and there be perfect friendship, this counts for five Gunas; or four if only common friendship. If there be friendship with an enemy of the other person it reduces the value to one Guna, and if both have such friendship to one half. In cases of mutual indifference the Gunas amount to three, and if there be mutual enmity there is no Guna.

6. Groups as in Table III. If both belong to the same group, six Gunas are present; also if the bridegroom belong to the god-group and the bride to the man-group. The reverse reduces it five: if the bridegroom be of demon-group, and the bride of god-group, there is only one Guna, and in all other cases none.

7. Kŭta, that is the agreement of the zodiacal signs and asterisms of bride and bridegroom. It is of two kinds, auspicious and ill-omened. The Kŭta is fortunate if the

bride and bridegroom be born in the same sign, but in different asterisms, or in the same asterisms, but in different signs, or, lastly, in the same asterisms but in different quarters. A difference of seven asterisms is also auspicious; for instance, if the bridegroom's asterism be Ashvini (Table III.), and that of the bride Pushya. The same is the case with three, four, ten, and eleven asterisms, and with a second sign from an even sign; for instance, Cancer being the fourth is an even sign, and if the sign of one party be Cancer and the other Virgo, the Kŭta is auspicious. This is also the case with a sixth sign from an even sign; and an eighth and a twelfth from an odd sign. But a second sign, a fifth, a sixth, a ninth, and a twelfth from an odd sign, and an eighth from an even sign, are unfortunate Kŭtas. The Gunas of Leo and Virgo are both auspicious. If there be a fortunate Kŭta, and the sign of the bridegroom be remote from that of the bride, and if there be enmity between the classes of the two, this conjunction will represent six Gunas. If there be the same sign and different asterisms, or the same asterism and different signs, the Gunas number five. In an unfortunate Kŭta if there be friendship between the classes of the postulants, and the bride's asterism be remote from that of the bridegroom this counts for four Gunas; but if there be only a single condition, it reduces the requisites to one. In all other cases there is no Kŭta.

1. The Nádi or point of time. If the nádis of the bride and bridegroom be different, as *e. g.,* first and last, first and middle, last and middle, this conjunction represents eight Gunas. The requisites are nil when the Nádi is alike.

APPENDIX II.

Now is related the Rasáyana, or preparation of metals for medicinal purposes.

FIRST RECIPE.

For the curing of diseases caused by quicksilver.[1] Take sixty-four Tolas (each three drachms) of the juice of betel-plant (*piper betel*); mix with equal quantities of the juice of Bhringárajá (*eclipta prostrata*), juice of the Tulsi (*ocymum basilicum*=herb basil) and goat's milk; and rub the mixture into all parts of the body for two days, each day two pahárs (= six hours) followed by a cold bath.

SECOND RECIPE.

For reducing mercury to Bhasma (ashes=metallic oxide). Take of purified quicksilver and sulphur equal parts, and levigate with the sap of the Banyan-tree (*ficus indica*); place the preparation in an earthern pot over a slow fire and stir with a stick of the Banyan-tree for a whole day. If two Gunjas (= 1 $^5/_{10}$ grs. troy) of this

---

1 The Hindus are supposed to have introduced the internal use of mercury which, in the shape of corrosive sublimate, found its way to Europe. They must have soon discovered the hideous effects of its abuse: in countries like Central Africa, where mercury is unknown, Syphilis never attacks the bones of the nose or face. The remedy in the text can do neither good nor harm.

medicine be eaten at early morning in betel leaf; digestion is improved and the powers of copulation are increased.

THIRD RECIPE.

For preparing Hemagarbha, the Elixir vitæ which contains gold. Take three parts of purified quicksilver; one part and a half of sulphur; one part of gold; two parts of the ashes (metallic oxide) of copper and calx of pearls and coral, each one-tenth of a part. Levigate in a mortar for seven days with the juice of the Kumári (*aloe perfoliata,*) make into a ball, cover well with a piece of cotton cloth and place in an earthen vessel, containing a little sulphur: the mouth must be well closed, leaving for the escape of smoke a small hole which must be kept open with a needle if necessary. Set the vessel over a Váluka-yantra (bain marie, or sand-bath) under which a slow fire is kindled. After about half a Ghataká (= 12 minutes) the fire must be diminished and allowed to extinguish. Remove the ball and use as the doctor directs.

FOURTH RECIPE.

For reducing Haritál (Sansk, hartálaka, = sulphuret of arsenic, yellow orpiment) to ashes, or metallic oxide. Levigate yellow orpiment and knead it with the juice of the plant Nágar-jŭni (a Cyperus-grass.) Levigate again with the juice of the Pinpalli (*piper longum*) and the Piper betel for two days. Make balls of the preparation; dry in shade; then set in earthen vessel in a bain marie. A hot fire must be kept up till the orpiment is thoroughly "cooked," and allow the fire to diminish and extinguish. Remove the balls from the vessel and use in every disease.

FIFTH RECIPE.

For absorbing all other metals by purified mercury. Thoroughly levigate quicksilver with the juice of the "seven minor poisons," *viz.*, Arka (*Callotropis gigantea*) Sehunda (*Euphorbia*), Dhatura (Stramonium, white thorn-apple), Lángali (*Jussiœa repens*), Karavira (oleander or Soma[1]) and opium. By this means mercury loses its wings and cannot fly, while it gets a mouth and eats up every metal with speed.

SIXTH RECIPE.

A sovereign remedy against all diseases and death. Take Abhraka (tale) and levigate with the milky sap of the Arka for the space of a day. Then wrap up the preparation in Arka-leaves and boil in a heap of Gobar (cow dung) cakes about two feet thick. Repeat this boiling with fresh leaves for seven times, then infuse the preparation three times in a decoction of Parámbi Maráthi, the fibrous roots of the Banyan-tree. In this way the mineral is "killed;" its impurities are removed and it becomes nishchandra talc. Boil equal parts of this and Ghi (clarified butter) in an iron vessel till the butter is absorbed, and it is ready for use; it cures every complaint, including old age and death.

[1] So the Dictionaries, naming very different plants, Nerium odorum (with poisonous root) and the harmless holy Soma (Sercostamma). But Kara-vira is a word of many meanings.

INDEX.

PAGE

Abatement of menstruation 52
Amorousness in women, signs of 28
Aphrodisiacs 43
Ashva, or Horse-man, Table applicable to . . . 21
Astrology in connection with marriage . . . 131
Biting before coition 106
Breasts, recipes for enlarging 62
————————————hardening 63
Breath, the, during coition 112
Chandrakalá, Tables of the . . . 9, 11, 12, 13, 14
Characteristics of women of various lands . . . 33
Charms to reduce persons to submission . . . 72
————for fascinating others 73
Coition—see Congress
Conceiving, prescriptions for 53
Congress 19
———— minor distinctions in 22
———— enjoyments before 97
———— postures of 117
Cosmetics 58
Cow-posture in coition 124
Days of greatest enjoyment for the four classes of women 5
Drugs to render men and women submissive . . 69
Elephant posture in coition 124
Embraces before coition 97
Eternal enjoyments 97
Families, limitation of 57
Finger-nails, use of 103
Hair, cosmetics for 58
————————————bleaching 60
————————————renewing 61
————manipulation of 108

PAGE

Hand, use of, in excitements to desire . . . 111
Hours which give the highest enjoyment to women . 6
Indifference in women, signs of 28
Internal enjoyments 115
Kisses, various kinds of 100
Limitation of families 57
Love, magical collyriums to win 71
Magical collyriums for winning love 71
——————— versets having power of fascination . . 74
Manipulation before coition 103
———————————of the hair 108
Manipulation of the Padminí 11
————————————————Chitriní 12
————————————————Shankhiní 31
————————————————Hastiní 14
Mantras—see Magical
Marriage, astrology in connection with . . . 131
Medicines 38
Men and Women, different kinds of 51
——————————— different signs in 77
——————————— drugs to render submissive . . 60
Menstruation, abatement of 52
——————————— arrest of 52
Metals for medicinal purposes, preparation of . . 139
Miscarriage, recipes for 55
Mouth, unguents for the 67
Orders of Women 1
Passion in women, seats of 8
Personal Peculiarities of the Four Orders of Women . 2
Philters 73
Postures of congress 117
Prayogas to induce venereal paroxysm . . . 39
———————to delay orgasm of man 40
———————to enlarge the linga 46
Pregnancy, prescriptions for 56
Prescriptions to contract the Yoní 48
——————————— for conceiving 53
——————————— to limit families 57
——————————— to render man or woman submissive . 69
Preventatives 57
Purúsháyita-bhramara-bandha 126
Recipes to perfume the Yoní 50
——————— to destroy body-pile 51
——————— to enable a woman to attract her husband's love 70

PAGE

Remedies for arrest of menstruation   52
————— to abate menstruation   52
Seats of passion in women   8
Shasha, or Hare-man, Table applicable to   .   .   20
Signs in men and women   77
Skin, cosmetics for   61
Spells   38
Tables of the Chandrakalá   .   .   .   9, 11, 12, 13, 14
Touches, Table of   9
Unguents to breed love   64
Vashíkarana, art of   69
Vrishabha, or Bull-man, Table applicable to   .   .   21
Women, orders of   1
————— personal peculiarities of   .   .   .   2
————— their days of greatest enjoyment   .   .   5
————— seats of passion in   8
————— different kinds of   17
————— general qualities, characteristics, temperaments, &c., of   24
————— signs of amorousness   .   .   .   28
————— signs of indifference   28
————— prescriptions to render submissive   .   .   69
————— passions of, before and during congress   .   . 113—114
Yoní, recipes to perfume the   50

''ARS AMORIS INDICA''

PHARMACOPEIA "ARS AMORIS INDICA"

SKT — *Sanscrit.*

ENG — *English.*

PUNJ — *Punjabi.*

BENG — *Bengali.*

TAM — *Tamil.*

MAH — *Marathi.*

ABRUS PRECATORIUS.

SKT.—*Gunja* (VI. 71, 79).
ENG.—Jequirity.
HINDI & PUNJ.—*Ratti.*
BENG.—*Kunch.*
MAH.—*Gunja.*
TAM.—*Gundumani.*

Habitat—Throughout India, from the Himalayas down to Ceylon.

Parts used—Root, seed or fruit.

Action—Antiphlogistic.

Uses—The powder of the seeds, rubbed into a paste with a little water or honey, is applied to the bare skin in alopecia, in sciatica, etc. The root, dug out on Sunday, when tied round the waist and head of a pregnant woman, is said to be ecbolic. But this is very doubtful.

———

ACACIA CATECHU.

SKT.—*Marga-vriksha* (VII. 69).
ENG.—Black Catechu.
HINDI & PUNJ.—*Katha.*
BENG. & MAH.—*Khair.*
TAM.—*Voadalam, Karangalli, Kasku-kutta.*

Habitat—Common in the forests of India and Burma.

Parts used – *Kshara* or the extract called Catechu.

Action—Powerful astringent.

Uses—Catechu is the extract prepared from the wood by boiling it in water and in-spissating the decoction. Its chief use in India is as an ingredient of the packet of betel leaves chewed by the people. A small piece of catechu held in the mouth and allowed slowly to dissolve acts like an astringent lozenge and is of great service in hoarseness, relaxed sore throat, loss of voice, and diseases of the mouth, teeth and gums.

ACACIA SPECIOSA.

Skt.—*Sirisha* (VII. 50).
Eng.—Sirissa tree.
Hindi and Punj.—*Sirin.*
Beng.—*Siriz.*
Mah.—*Siras.*
Tam.—*Chireedam.*

Habitat—Sub-Himalayan tract, Bengal, Central and South India.

Parts used—Flowers.

Action—Astringent and cooling.

Uses—The flowers are fragrant and form an ingredient of fragrant unguents and cosmetics.

ACHYRANTHES ASPERA.

Skt.—*Khara-manjari* (VI. 34).
Eng.—Rough Chaff Tree, Prickly Chaff-flower.
Hindi.—*Latchira, Chrchira.*
Punj.—*Puth-kanda.*
Beng.—*Apang.*
Mah.—*Aghada, Pandhara-aghada.*
Tam.—*Shiru-kadaladi, Nayurivi.*

Habitat—A small herb found all over India.

Parts used—The herb and its seed.

Action—Astringent and alterative.

Uses—It forms an ingredient of medicated oils for local application in weakened and relaxed nerves, primary syphilitic sores, etc., etc.

ACORUS COLAMU

Skt.—*Vacha* (VI. 31, 45, 88, 90, 93 ; VII. 4, 27).
Eng.—Sweet-flag.
Hindi, Punj. and Beng.—*Bach.*

Mah.—*Vekhana.*
Tam.—*Vasambu.*

Habitat—A semi-aquatic perennial herb growing in damp, marshy place, and indigenous to India and Burma.

Parts used—The dried rhizome.

Action—The root is stimulant an aromatic.

Uses—Its powder is used externally in chronic rheumatism. With other ingredients it is useful for acne, sycosis and pimples, for bracing up the relaxed breasts, contracting the vagina and invigorating the male organ.

AEGLE MARMELOS.

Skt.—*Sri-phala* (VII. 40), *Bilva* (VII. 46, 51).
Eng.—Bael fruit.
Hindi.—*Bel.*
Punj.—*Bil.*
Beng.—*Bela.*
Mah.—*Bael.*
Tam.—*Vilvum.*

Habitat—Found all over India, from sub-Himalayan forests to Central and South India.

Parts used—The fruit, the root-bark and the leaves.

Action—The fruit is alterative and nutritive. The leaves and root-bark are aromatic and cooling.

Uses—The leaves and the root-bark are used in cosmetics.

AGASTI GRANDIFLORA.

Skt.—*Agastya* (VI. 8).
Hindi.—*Agasta-patra.*
Beng.—*Buko.*
Mah.—*Agasti.*
Tam.—*Akatti.*

Habitat—Cultivated in South and West India, in the Ganges valley and in Bengal.

Parts used—The leaves.

Action—The leaves being astringent, their juice promotes circulation and invigorates the parts to which it is applied.

Uses—The juice of the leaves mixed with other ingredients is recommended here for local application to the male organ before coitus with a view to cause early orgasm in the woman. The poultice of the leaves is a popular remedy for bruises.

ALOE LITORALIS.

SKT.—*Kanya* (VII. 10).
ENG.—Small aloe.
HINDI.—*Chhota-kanvar.*
PUNJ.=*Elwa.*
BENG.—*Ananash.*
MAH.—*Lahani kumari, Kalaboel.*
TAM.—*Chirukattalai, Kariambolam.*

Habitat—This has become quite naturalised on the Southern coast of the Madras Presidency.

Parts used—The leaves and the juice from transversely cut leaves inspissated by heat or solidified without the aid of heat.

Action—Tonic.

Uses—The pulp of the leaves well washed in cold water is prescribed as a refrigerant medicine in conjunctivitis, with a small quantity of sugar-candy. The same pulp, so purified, with the addition of a little burnt alum is considered a valuable application in cases of ophthalmia.

ALSTONIA SCHOLARIS.

SKT.—*Sapta-parna* (VI. 17; VII. 45),
    Sapta-chchhada (VII. 16).
ENG.—Dita Bark.
HINDI and PUNJ.—*Satauna.*
BENG.—*Chhatin.*
MAH.—*Satveen.*
TAM.—*Aelilappalai, Wodrasi.*

Habitat—Common throughout India.

Parts used—The seed and the bark.

Action—Stimulant, bitter tonic, astringent and aphrodisiac.

Uses—The seeds are aphrodisiac and are used in medicines for increasing retentive power during sexual intercourse. The powder of the bark is used in cosmetics.

AMOORA ROHITAKA (?).

SKT.—*Mamsa* (VII. 62).
HINDI.—*Rohera.*
BENG.—*Rodha, Rayana, Kadar.*
MAH.—*Rakta-rohida.*
TAM.—*Mulumodugachettu.*

Habitat—It is generally found in forests. It is of two kinds, one bearing white and the other red flowers.

Parts used—Flowers.

Action—Bitter, astringent and cooling.

Uses—The flowers are used in perfumes and cosmetics.

ANDROPOGON MURICATUS.

SKT.—*Usira* (VII. 44, 47, 50, 54, 56, 57).
ENG.—The Cuscus grass.
HINDI and PUNJ.—*Kha*s.
BENG.—*Khaskhas.*
MAH.—*Vala.*
TAM.—*Vettivaer.*

Habitat—Coromandal Coast, Mysore, Bengal, Rajputana and Chhota Nagpur.

Parts used—The fibrous wiry roots from the rhizome.

Action—Tonic, stimulant, diaphoretic and cooling.

Uses—Externally the paste of the root is rubbed on the skin to remove oppressive heat or burning of the body. By mixing it with red sandal wood and other fragrant ingredients into a tub of water an aromatic bath is prepared. It is also used in cosmetics.

ANTHOCEPHALUS CADAMBA.

SKT.—*Kadamba.* (VI. 75 ; VII. 29).
HINDI, PUNJ. and BENG.—*Kadamba.*
MAH.—*Raja Kadamba, Bhumi Kadamba.*
TAM.—*Vella Kadamba.*

Habitat—All over India.

Parts used—The fruit and the flowers.

Action—The fruit is refrigerant and anti-bilious.

Uses —The fruit, in conjunction with other things, is said to be contraceptive.

AQUILARIA AGALLOCHA.

SKT.—*Aguru* (VII. 47, 57, 63).
ENG.—Aloe-wood.
HINDI and BENG.—*Agaru*.
PUNJ.—*Agar*.

Habitat—Assam, East Himalaya, Bhutan and Kassia mountains.

Parts used—The wood.

Action—Aromatic.

Uses—Used as a perfume in the form of powder. It is one of the chief ingredients in incense sticks.

ARSENICUM RUBRUM.

SKT.—*Sila* (VI. 33 ; VII. 10, 13).
ENG.—Realgar or Red Orpiment.
HINDI and PUNJ.—*Mansil, Lal Hartal*.
MAH.—*Manasil*.
TAM.—*Kudire-palpashanam*.

Character—Realgar is artificially prepared by fusing arsenious acid 5 parts with sulphur 3 parts. It is purified by being rubbed with the juice of lemons or of ginger.

Action—Alternative and tonic. When applied externally it promotes the circulation of blood.

Uses—As liniment or in oils it is used for local application to stimulate the circulation of blood and thus restore the broken down and dead tissues. *Chakradatta* recommends it for application to the eye in affections of the internal tunics, tumours or other growths, night-blindness, etc.

ASPARAGUS RACEMOSUS.

SKT.—*Sata-patra* (VI. 23, 28), *Satavari* (VI. 85).
HINDI, PUNJ. and MAH.—*Satavar*.
BENG.—*Satmuli*.
TAM.—*Faniyanaku*.

Habitat—This climber is found all over India.

Parts used—The root and its juice.

Action—Nutritive, tonic, demulcent and aphrodisiac.

Uses—The *Satavari ghrita* is prepared from the fresh root-juice, honey, ghee, milk and sugar and is used as an aphrodisiac tonic. Other preparations of the root are also said to increase the secretion of semen, to cure barrenness in women and to remove disorders of female genitals.

ASTERACANTHA LONGIFOLIA.

SKT.—*Kokila-vriksha* (VI. 16), *Pikakhya* [VI. 19], *Pikaksha* [VI. 42, 27].
HINDI and PUNJ.—*Talamakhana* [the seed].
BENG.—*Kanta kokila*.
MAH.—*Kolsunda*.
TAM.—*Neerumulli*.

Habitat—This little annual plant is common in most places on the banks of the tanks, ditches, pools, etc., throughout India and Ceylon.

Parts used—The seed.

Action—The seeds are tonic, aphrodisiac and refrigerant.

Uses.—The seeds are given with sugar, milk or wine in doses of 1 to 3 *dirhems* for impotence. Combined with *Gokhru* and *Musli*, they are taken in powder form, with cow's milk and sugar for general debility. A confection of the seeds containing a large number of aphrodisiac, demulcent, nutritious and aromatic stimulant substances, has been in use for impotence, seminal and other debilities. Their paste is said to contract the vagina.

AURUM.

SKT.—*Kanchana* [VI. 56].
ENG.—Gold.
HINDI, PUNJ. and MAH.—*Sona*.
BENG.—*Sonar*.
TAM.—*Ponnu*.

Source—Found in primitive rocks, and in alluvial deposits, in small particles called the gold dust.

Character—Pure gold has a metallic lustre and reddish yellow colour. It is the most ductile of all metals softer than silver. It acquires lustre under pressure.

Action—Gold and its preparations are nervine and aprodisiac tonic, resolvent and alterative. They are said to increase strength and beauty, improve intellect and memory, clear the voice and increase sexual power. They also increase the flow of menses in women.

Uses—Preparations of properly reduced gold *(Kanchana-bhasma)* are used in diseases of the nervous system and urinary organs, hysteria, epilepsy, amenorrhœa, impotence, sterility, habitual abortion, etc., etc.

AZADIRACHTA INDICA.

SKT.—*Nimba* [VI. 84 ; VII. 45], *Pichumanda* [VII. 49].
ENG.—The *Neem* or Margosa tree.
HINDI, PUNJ. and BENG.—*Nim.*
MAH.—*Kadunimba.*
TAM.—*Vembu.*

Habitat—Indigenous to and cultivated nearly all over India and Burma.

Parts used—The seed and the leaves.

Action—The young fruit is astringent and tonic. The oil from the seeds contains margosic acid, glycerides of fatty acids, butyric acid and a trace of valeric acid detected as volatile acids, a small quantity of natural resin, etc. It is local stimulant, insecticide and antiseptic. The leaves are discutient, and cooling.

Uses—The oil taken internally in small doses is said to turn black the grey hair. The paste of the leaves is used externally in cases of small pox. When applied to the body with other cosmetics, it is cooling, invaluable in febrile cases, antiseptic and useful in skin diseases.

BAMBUSA ARUNDINACEAE.

SKT.—*Venu* [VI. 55].
ENG.—Bamboo.

HINDI, BENG. and PUNJ.—*Bans.*
MAH.—*Bamboo.*
TAM.—*Moongil.*

Habitat—Common in Central and South India, cultivated in Bengal and North-Western India.

Parts used—Young leaves or shoots.

Action—The leaves are emmenagogue.

Uses—The leaf-bud is administered in decoction to encourage the free discharge of the menses or lochia after delivery, when it is scanty.

BASSIA LATIFOLIA

SKT.—*Madhuka.* [VI. 46, 69].
ENG.—The Indian Butter tree, Mahwa tree.
HINDI and PUNJ.—*Jangli Mohwa.*
BENG.—*Maua.*
MAH.—*Mowda.*
TAM.—*Madhookam Illupai.*

Habitat—Bombay Presidency, Bengal and South Indian forests and Ceylon.

Parts used—The pith of the wood and the bark.

Action—Alterative, stimulant, astringent tonic and cooling.

Uses—Here the powder of the heartwood is recommended for contracting the relaxed vagina and the bark is declared to be ecbolic.

BERBERIS ARISTATA.

SKT.—*Anjana* [VI. 48], *Rasanjana,* [VI. 54], *Tarkshyam* [VII. 27].
ENG.—Indian Barberry, Ophthalmic Barberry, Tree-turmeric.
HINDI and PUNJ.—*Rasaut.*
BENG.—*Dar-haldi.*
MAH.—*Daru-halad.*
TAM.—*Maramanjal, Kasturi-manjal.*

Habitat—The barberry bushes grow on the Nilgiris and all over the temperate Himalaya, from Bhutan to Kunawer.

Parts used—The crude extract prepared

from the root-bark.

Action—Tonic, astringent, diaphoretic and alterative.

Uses—A decoction of the extract and other medicines such as emblic myrobalan, Bael fruit, etc., is given in leucorrhœa, menorrhagia etc.

BLACK SALT.

SKT.—*Krishna-lavana* [VI. 36].
HINDI.—*Padelon, Kala lun.*
BENG.—*Kale nun.*
MAH.—*Kalo-mith.*
PUNJ.—*Sanchal lun.*

Character—It is also called *Vid-Lavana* in Sanskrit. It is either prepared by evaporation from saline soil or is artificially prepared by fusing fossil salt with a small portion of Emblic myrobalan, the product being muriate of soda with small quantities of muriate of lime, sulphur and oxide of iron.

Action—Tonic, stomachic, etc.

Uses—Here it is used as an ingredient of a medicine for increasing the size of the male organ.

BOERHAVIA PROCUMBENS.

SKT.—*Varsha-bhu* [VI. 13].
ENG.—Spreading hog-weed.
HINDI.—*Beshakapore.*
PUNJ.—*Itsit.*
BENG.—*Gandhapurna, Swetapoorna.*
MAH.—*Punanava, Khapra.*
TAM.—*Mookkiratti, Kadiyirattam.*

Habitat—Found all over India. It is of two kinds, one with white and the other with red flowers. The former is used in medicine.

Parts used—The root.

Action—Bitter.

Uses—The powder of the dried root, when applied to the soles of the feet, is claimed to delay ejaculation during sexual intercourse, but its efficacy for the purpose is very doubtful.

BOMBAX MALABARICUM.

SKT.—*Salmali.* [VI. 89.].
ENG.—Silk cotton tree, Seemul tree.
HINDI.—*Narma, Simbal.*
BENG.—*Rakta simal.*
MAH.—*Tambdi-savaru, Sauri.*
TAM.—*Elevam.*

Habitat—Throughout the hotter forest regions of India. Cultivated also in gardens.

Parts used—The thorns.

Action—Demulcent and slightly astringent.

Uses—Used externally for inflammations and cutaneous eruptions in the form of a paste.

BRASSICA ALBA.

SKT.—*Siddhartha* [VI. 90, 91 ; VII. 11].
ENG.—White mustard.
HINDI.—*Sufed-rai.*
BENG.—*Dhop-rai.*
MAH.—*Mohori-pandri.*
TAM.—*Kadugu.*

Habitat—Extensively cultivated in India. Indigenous to Western Asia.

Parts used—The seed and oil.

Action—The whole plant is considered to possess bitter, aperient and tonic properties. The oil is stimulant and counter-irritant.

Uses—The seeds, mixed with other medicines in the form of a paste, form an efficient counter-irritant application. They are also useful in urticaria, acne, etc. The oil is used in lamps, and as an embrocation.

BUTEA FRONDOSA.

SKT.—*Palasa* [VI. 51 ; VII. 29, 32].
ENG.—Bastard teak.
HINDI, BENG. and MAH.—*Palash.*
PUNJ.—*Dhak.*
TAM.—*Murukkanmaram.*

Habitat—Mountainous districts of India and Burma and common all over Bengal.

Parts used—Ashes of the burnt bark

and wood and flowers.

Action—The bark contains kino-tannic and gallic acids.

Uses—The ashes are used in depilatories.

CAESALPINIA BONDUC (?).

Skt.—*Putika* [VII. 58].
Eng.—Molucca bean, Bonduc seed, Fever nut.
Hindi.—*Sagar-ghota, Lalkaranj.*
Beng.—*Nata Karanj, Natar-phal.*
Mah.—*Gajago.*

Habitat—A climbing shrub common throughout India.

Parts used—The seed and the root-bark.

Action—Bitter tonic and febrifuge.

Uses—The powder of the seeds and root-bark is used in fragrant unguents for the body.

CALOTROPIS GIGENTA.

Skt.—*Arka*. [VI. 97 ; VII. 4].
Eng.—Gigantic Swallow-wort.
Hindi—*Ak, madar.*
Punj.—*Akka.*
Beng.—*Akanda.*
Mah.—*Ruvi, Akda.*
Tam.—*Badabadam, Erukku.*

Habitat—These shrubs are found chiefly in waste lands.

Parts used—The milky juice and the root-bark of the white blossomed variety.

Action—The physiologically active substance is found in the milky juice of the plant. The drug acts like digitalis on the heart. It increases secretions especially the evacuation of bile and has a sedative action on the muscular fibres of the intestines. The juice is a violent gastro-intestinal irritant. For medicinal purposes the root-bark should be selected from plants as old as possible.

Uses—The milky juice forms an ingredient of the unguent for bracing up the fallen breasts of women. The powder of the root

bark with other drugs, when mixed with menstrual discharge and applied on the forehead, is said to possess occult powers of infatuating others.

CAMPHORA OFFICINARUM.

Skt.—*Karpura* [VI. 7, 15 ; VII. 24, 53, 56, 63, 67], *Ghana-Sara* [VII. 23] and *Chandra* [VII. 58, 60].
Eng.—Camphor.
Hindi, Punj., Beng. and Mah.—*Kapur.*
Tam.—*Karpooram.*

Habitat—It is generally imported from China and Japan where the trees grow.

Parts used—The concrete volatile oil, *i. e,* camphor, obtained from the wood by distillation. It occurs in translucent white crystals.

Action—Stimulant, antiseptic, expectorant, temporary aphrodisiac and externally anodyne, and diaphoretic. It also promotes circulation.

Uses—Camphor is of a very peculiar fragrant and penetrating odour, bitter, pungent and aromatic taste. A piece held in the mouth makes it fragrant, and is said to be a protective against fevers and other infectious diseases. In cases of spermatorrhœa, chordee, pruritus, etc., pills of camphor and opium, taken at bed time are found to be very efficacious.

CARTHAMUS TINCTORIUS.

Skt.—*Kusumbha* [VI. 13].
Eng.—Shafflower.
Hindi and Punj.—*Kasumbha.*
Beng. – *Kajireh.*
Mah.—*Kardi.*
Tam.—*Sendurkam, kusumba-virai.*

Habitat—Tropical and sub-tropical parts of India.

Parts used—Oil from the seed [*Kausumbha-tailam*].

Action—The seeds are purgative.

Uses—The oil is edible and is also used in manufacturing soaps. Here it is alleged to effect the retention of the seminal fluid during intercourse, when applied to the soles of the feet before union. But that is very doubtful.

CELATRUS PANICULATUS.

SKT.—*Jyotishmati* [VI. 52].
ENG.—Staff tree.
HINDI and PUNJ.—*Malkangani.*
MAH.—*Kanguni.*
TAM.—*Atiparichcham.*

Habitat=Hilly districts, Himalayas and Ceylon.

Parts used—The leaves.

Action—The roasted leaves are emmenagogue.

Uses—The roasted leaves together with flowers of China Rose, rubbed in water, are taken to restore menstrual flow.

CINNAMOMUM CASSIA.

SKT.—*Tvak-patra* [VII. 65].
ENG.—Cinnamon.
HINDI, PUNJ., BENG. and MAH.—*Dalchini.*
TAM.—*Lowanga-patta.*

Habitat—Indigenous to Ceylon and Southern India.

Parts used—The dried inner bark of the shoots from truncated stalks [*cinnamoni cortex*].

Action—The bark is aromatic, stimulant, astringent, antiseptic and germicide.

Uses—It is very largely used as a spice. It is a frequent ingredient of pill-masses. It strengthens the gums and perfumes the breath. Its oil is applied in tooth-ache.

CINNAMOMUM INERS.

SKT.—*Patraka* [VII. 53], *Patra* VII. 55, 57].
HINDI.—*Tejpatra, Jangli darchini.*
PUNJ.—*Tejpat.*
MAH.—*Ranchadal.*
TAM.—*Kattu-kurrnap.*

Habitat—Tropical and sub-tropical Himalayas, U. P., Bengal and Burma.

Parts used—The leaves.

Action—Stimulant, diaphoretic and deobstruent.

Uses—The leaves are largely used as a condiment. They are also used in making the baths fragrant and in preparing cosmetics for the body. The oil distilled from the leaves is used in flavouring sweets and confectionery.

CITRUS MEDICA.

SKT.—*Bijapura* (VI. 61) *Matulanga* (VI. 69.)
ENG.—Citron.
HINDI—*Maphal.*
PUNJ.—*Bajaura.*
BENG.—*Chholongo Nebu.*
MAH.—*Madala.*
TAM.—*Madee phalamu.*

Habitat—It is a garden plant chiefly cultivated for its valuable fruit and met with chiefly in the South-West of India.

Parts used—The root and the rind.

Action—Expellant of poisons, aromatic and stomachic. The rind is hot, dry and tonic.

Uses—It is taken with advantage in cases of hæmorrhage from the stomach, bowels, uterus, kidney and other internal organs. It is also claimed to be ecbolic.

COCCULUS CORDIFOLIOUS.

SKT.—*Amrita* (VI. 58).
ENG.—Heart-leaved moon-seed.
HINDI and PUNJ.—*Galo.*
BENG.—*Gulancha.*
MAH.—*Gulvel.*
TAM.—*Sindilkodi, Amradvalli.*

Habitat—A common climbing shrub growing on *Nim* and other high trees in tropical Western India, Burma and Ceylon.

Parts used—The stem (preferably in fresh state).

Action—Stomachic, bitter tonic, alterative, aphrodisiac, hepatic stimulant, antiperiodic, mild diuretic and demulcent.

Uses—It is very valuable tonic and is

best given in infusion. The tincture is useful in general and seminal debility, leucorrhœa, etc., etc.

CONJEE WATER.

SKT.—*Tusha-toya* (VI. 74.), *Tandul-ambhas* (VI. 76), *Aranalaka* (VI. 83), and *Tandula-toya* (VI. 99).

ENG.—Sour rice gruel.

HINDI, PUNJ. and BENG.—*Kanji, Dhanka-pani.*

Source—Prepared from the rice by boiling them in water and allowing the water to frement.

Action—Rice-water or *conjee* is demulcent and refrigerant.

Uses—A good drink for an irritable or inflammatory state of the stomach, bowels or kidneys. Rice-water is also prescribed as a vehicle for some powders and confections.

CROCUS SATIVUS.

SKT.—*Kunkuma* [VII 25, 56].
ENG.—Saffron.
HINDI and PUNJ.—*Kesar.*
BENG.—*Jafran, Kesara.*
MAH.—*Keshar.*
TAM.—*Kunkum-pu.*

Habitat—An autumnal dwarf herb, a native of Levant in Asia Minor, now cultivated on a small scale in Kashmir.

Parts used—The dried stigmata and tops of the styles of *Crocus Sativus.*

Action—It has a peculiar aromatic odour and a bitter, pungent taste. It is stimulant, stomachic and slightly anodyne.

Uses—It is used generally as a condiment for its aromatic odour and beautiful curlo oingmatter. It is also used in incense and cosmetics.

CUMINUM CYMINUM.

SKT.—*Dvi-jira* [VI. 91], *i. e.* the two kinds of *jira.*

ENG.—Cumin seed.
HINDI, PUNJ. and BENG.—*Safed jira.*
MAH.—*Jeera.*
TAM.—*Cheerakam.*

Habitat—Extensively cultivated in Northern India and the Punjab; also imported from Persia and Asia Minor.

Parts used—The seed.

Action—Aromatic, stimulant and stomachic.

Uses—This, along with the black variety mentioned below, is used externally in the form of poultice, oil or paste for eczema and other skin diseases. In the text it is recommended for removing black spots from the face.

CUMINUM NIGRUM.

SKT.—*Jira* [VI. 91].
ENG.—Black cumin or Small Fennel.
HINDI and PUNJ.—*Kala-jira.*
BENG.—*Mugrela.*
MAH.—*Krishna-jiragam.*
TAM.—*Karun-jiragam.*

Habitat—Cultivated in some parts of India

Parts used—The seed.

Action—Aromatic, carminative, stimulant, astringent and diaphoretic. Locally its oil is anæsthetic.

Uses—Along with the other variety mentioned above, it is recommended for removing black spots from the face.

CUPRUM.

SKT.—*Tamra* [VI. 56].
ENG.—Copper.
HINDI and PUNJ.—*Tamba.*
BENG.—*Tama.*
MAH.—*Tambe.*
TAM.—*Shembu.*

Source—Found extensively free in metallic state and also in various combinations. Copper ore is found in the districts of Singbhum and Hazaribag [Bengal].

Character—A brilliant, sonorous, ductile metal of a reddish colour. It is used in its reduced or calcined form *(tamra-bhasma)* which is a dark black powder, somewhat gritty to feel.

Action—Astringent, sedative, alterative, antiseptic, emetic and purgative.

Uses—The *bhasma* enters in the composition of medicines for phthisis, enlarged spleen, purifying the womb, etc.

CURCUMA LONGA.

SKT.—*Nisa* [VI. 45], *Yuvati*, [VII. 27]. *Nisha-yugma* [VI. 41] and *Nisha-dvayam* [VI 92, 97], *i. e.* the 2 kinds of *Nisa* [see also *Curcuma Zedoaria*].
ENG.—Turmeric.
HINDI and PUNJ.—*Haldi.*
BENG. and MAH.—*Halad.*
TAM.—*Manjal.*

Habitat—Extensively cultivated all over India.

Parts used—The tubers or rhizomes.
Action—Aromatic, stimulant and tonic.

Uses—The root is used both internally and externally in skin diseases. A paste of turmeric and the leaves of *Justicia Adhatoda* with cow's milk is rubbed on the skin in prurigo. Mixed with gingelly oil it is applied to the body to prevent skin eruptions. It also forms an ingredient of incense.

CURCUMA ZEDOARIA.

SKT.—*Sati* [VII 55].
ENG.—The round Zedoary.
HINDI and PUNJ.—*Kachur.*
BENG.—*Sutha, Sati.*
MAH.—*Kuv, Kachur.*
TAM.—*Kastori-manjal, Nirvisham.*

Habitat—Cultivated in gardens in many parts of India.
Parts used—The tubers and the leaves.
Action—Stimulant, demulcent and rubefacient.

Uses—The root possesses agreeable, camphoraceous smell. The pounded root is applied as a paste to the body. It is an odoriferous ingredient of the cosmetics used for the cure of chronic skin diseases caused by impure or deranged blood.

CYPERUS PERTENUIS.

SKT.—*Mustam* (VII. 4), *Ambuda* (VII. 53, 56), *Ghana* (VII. 54, 58), *Toyada*, (VII. 55, 60), *Ambhoda* (VII 62).
ENG.—Indian Cyperus.
HINDI, PUNJ., and BENG.—*Nagaramotha.*
MAH.—*Lavala.*
TAM.—*Mutta-kachi.*

Habitat—Damp places in Bengal.

Parts used—The tubers.

Action—Refrigerant, aromatic and alterative.

Uses—The root yields an oil which is used as hair tonic and perfume. It is also used in the preparation of medicated oils and cosmetics.

DATURA ALBA.

SKT.—*Kanaka* (VI. 10 ; VII. 24, 58), *Kanchana* (VI. 58), *Svarna* VII. 53, 62, 65).
ENG.—Thorn-apple.
HINDI, PUNJ., and BENG.—*Dhatoora.*
TAM.—*Umattai.*

Habitat—This plant exists in different species, distinguished by the colour of its flowers. These species are found growing commonly in waste places throughout India, from Kashmir to Malabar.

Parts used—The seed and the leaves.

Action—It has narcotic, anodyne and antispasmodic properties analogous to those of belladonna.

Uses—The seeds are useful as astringent in skin diseases and as local stimulant.

ECHITES FRUTESCENS.

SKT.—*Syamalata* (VI. 97).
ENG.—Black creeper.

HINDI—*Dudhi-lata.*
BENG.—*Shama-lata.*
MAH.—*Kante bhouri.*
TAM.—*Nellatiga.*

Habitat—It is a climbing plant found throughout India.

Parts used—The roots, stalk and leaves.

Action—The root is an alterative tonic, diuretic and diaphoretic.

Uses—It is used in the treatment of skin diseases and eruptions. It also enters into the composition of oils for bracing up the relaxed breasts.

ELAEOCARPUS GANITRUS.

SKT.—*Sivaksha* (VII. 16).
HINDI, PUNJ., and BENG.—*Rudraksha.*

Habitat—Ceylon and Africa.

Parts used—The stone of the fruit or the seed.

Uses—The seeds are commonly used for making rosaries for counting prayers. Here they are used in connection with a magical rite for infatuating the beloved person.

ELETTARIA CARDAMOMUM.

SKT.—*Ela* (VII. 27, 53, 55, 65.)
ENG.—Lesser cardamom.
HINDI and PUNJ.—*Chhoti Elaichi.*
BENG.—*Garate, Chota Elaichi.*
MAH.—*Valdode, Elaichi.*
TAM.—*Elakaya.*

Habitat—Cultivated for its fruit in many parts of Southern India and Ceylon.

Parts used—The dried ripe seed.

Action—Powerful aromatic, stimulant, carminative, diuretic.

Uses—The cardamom seeds are generally used as a masticatory to make the mouth fragrant. They are also employed as an ingredient of cosmetics, incense and toilet preparations.

EMBLICA OFFICINALIS.

SKT.—*Dhatri* (VI. 22, 54, 66, 87; VII. 54).

ENG.—Emblic myrobalan; Indian goose-berry.
HINDI and PUNJ.—*Aunla, Amla.*
BENG.—*Amlak, Amla.*
MAH.—*Avala.*
TAM.—*Toppi.*

Habitat—The Deccan, the sea-coast districts and Kashmir.

Parts used—The dried fruit, and the fresh fruit.

Action—The fresh fruit is refrigerant, diuretic and laxative. The dried fruit is astringent.

Uses—The juice of the fresh fruit and *ghee* mixed together is a good restorative tonic. The powder of the dried fruit given with ghee and honey is a restorative invigorator, especially in winter days.

Half a drachm each of the emblic seed *gokhru,* powdered and mixed with 5 grains of *Gulancha* and given early morning in *ghee* and sugar is an equally nutrient tonic.

The dried fruit is also useful in leucorrhœa and other uterine complaints.

A fixed oil obtained from the berries strengthens and promotes the growth of hair, and the essential oil from the leaves is used in perfumery.

EUGENIA JAMBOLANA.

SKT.—*Jambu* (VI. 43; VII. 48).
ENG.—The rose-apple tree, Jambul, the Black Plum tree.
HINDI.—*Jaman.*
BENG.—*Kala jam.*
MAH.—*Jambul.*
TAM.—*Nagum, Navel.*

Habitat—Throughout the plains from the Himalayas to South India.

Parts used—The bark and the seed.

Action—Astringent.

Uses—A paste of the bark is applied over inflamed parts. Being an astringent, it acts as a contractile on the tissues. The seed is used in cosmetics, etc.

EUPHORBIA NERIFOLIA.

SKT.=*Vajri* [VI. 12, 87], *Snuhi* [VI. 86].
ENG.—Common Milk-hedge.
HINDI and PUNJ.—*Danda Thohar.*
BENG.—*Manasasij.*
MAH.—*Vayinvadunga, Thora.*
TAM.—*Ilaikkalli.*

Habitat—The shrub is found in Central India and cultivated in Bengal.

Parts used—The milky juice

Action—Irritant, rubefacient and vesicant.

Uses—When applied to the soles of the feet, the juice is said to promote retention. But this is very doubtful.

FEL BOVINUM PURIFICATUM.

SKT.—*Gorochana* [VI. 85; VII. 8], *Rochana* [VII. 10, 13, 24].
ENG.—A bright yellow orpiment prepared from the bile of cattle, Serpent-stone, Gall-stone.
HINDI, BENG., PUNJ., MAH.—*Gorochan.*
TAM.—*Gorojanai.*

Source—It is said to be a concretion found in the stomach and in the gall-bladder of an ox or cow, and occurs as light, and yellowish or green, solid or spherical concretions.

Action—Laxative, cooling and aromatic.

Uses—It enters into the composition of some medicines used for skin diseases and in hair-dyes.

FERONIA ELEPHANTUM.

SKT.—*Kapittha* (VI. 55).
ENG.—Elephant or Wood-apple.
HINDI.—*Kavat.*
PUNJ.—*Kainth.*
BENG.—*Kathbel.*
MAH.—*Kavitpana.*
TAM.—*Vilakapittam, Vilaphalam.*

Habitat—Met with throughout India, cultivated for its fruit.

Parts used—The pulp of the fruit.

Action—The fruit is aromatic, astringent (when unripe), and refrigerant.

Uses—It is said to stop excessive menstrual flow, when given in combination with bamboo-leaves and honey.

FERRI SULPHÁS

SKT.—*Kasisa* (VI. 38).
ENG.—Green vitriol, Iron sulphate, Green sulphate of iron.
HINDI and PUNJ.—*Hira Kasis.*
BENG.—*Hira kasa.*
TAM.—*Annabhedi.*

Source—It is a salt usually obtained by the decomposition of iron-pyrites by the action of atmospheric moisture. It can also be obtained by dissolving iron wires in sulphuric acid by the aid of heat.

Character—It occurs in pale-bluish green, oblique, rhombic prisms.

Action—The taste is very astringent or styptic, and without any odour. It has an acid reaction.

Uses—Externally iron sulphate is used in skin diseases either alone or with other medicines. *Chakradatta* and *Sarngadhara* both recommend an oil called the *Kasisadaya taila*, as an application to the genitals and the breasts with a view to strengthen them.

FERRUM.

SKT.—*Aya*s [VI. 29], *Rukma* [VI. 56].
ENG.—Iron.
HINDI, PUNJ. and BENG.—*Loha.*
MAH.—*Lokhand.*
TAM.—*Irimbu.*

Source—Rarely met with free in nature. Found in nearly all rocks, soils, etc., variously combined with oxygen, sulphur, and other things.

Character—Iron has to be purified before using it in medicines. It is of several varieties. In preparation of medicines the *kanta* (*i. e.* wrought iron) variety is generally recommended. It possesses one, two, three, four, or five faces and often many more [with which to attract iron] and is of yellow, black and red colour respectively.

Preparation—Reduced iron *Lauha bhasma* or *Mritayas* is an oxide of iron, the most easy method of preparing which is by soaking it for seven successive days in the juice of the leaves of *Eugenia Jambolana*, and drying it in the sun. Then the iron is roasted [by *putas*] as usual. Six to ten *putas* are sufficient for the efficient reduction of iron.

Action—Iron improves the quality of blood, produces constipation and stimulates the functional activity of all the organs of the body and is therefore a valuable general tonic. The *Bhasma* is a powerful alterative, astringent, tonic and restorative.

Uses—Iron is of great value in both simple and secondary anæmias. It enters into the composition of various *rasas* which are useful in urinary diseases, female complaints, etc.

FICUS INDICA.

Skt.—*Vata* [VI. 19].
Eng.—The Banyan tree.
Hindi.—*Bar.*
Punj.—*Borh.*
Beng.—*Bar, Bargat.*
Mah.—*Vata vriksha.*
Tam.—*Alamaram.*

Habitat—This well-known tree is wild in the lower Himalayas and is now found all over India.

Parts used—The milky juice.

Action—Tonic and astringent.

Uses—The fresh juice on a piece of loaf sugar, or in combination with other medicines, is aphrodisiac and is also believed to be of much value in spermatorrhœa and gonorrhœa.

FLACOURTIA CATAPHRACTA.

Skt.—*Talisa* [VII. 11].
Hindi—*Talispatri. Paniamlak.*
Beng.—*Paniyala.*

Mah.—*Taleespatra, Panambale.*
Tam.—*Talisapatram.*

Habitat—Found in Bengal, Nepal to Assam, Chittagong and on the sea coasts of India.

Parts used—The leaves.

Action—The dried leaves are stomachic, tonic and astringent.

Uses—The dried leaves are useful in asthma, bronchitis, phthisis and catarrh of the bladder, but here it forms a constituent of the collyrium used for infatuating others.

GALEGA PURPUREA.

Skt.—*Ishupunkha* [VI. 18].
Hindi—*Sarphenka.*
Punj.—*Bansa,* [called *Mahan* on the Barnala side].
Beng.—*Bannil gachh.*
Mah.—*Unhali.*
Tam.—*Kolluk-kay-velai.*

Habitat—Found throughout India.

Parts used—The root.

Action—Deobstruent, diuretic and useful in cough and other chest complaints.

Uses—Here the root is claimed to increase the retentive power when tied round the waist during the sex act.

GASTEROPODA.

Skt., Hindi, Punj., and Mah.—*Sankha* [VI. 50].
Eng.—Conch, Chank.
Tam.—*Sanka, sangu.*

Source—Indian Ocean coasts.

Character—A porcelaneous shell of an oblong or conical form. The upper surface is highly tuberculated, the under surface shining, very brittle and translucent.

Preparation—*Sankha bhasma* or conch shell ash [silicate of magnesia]. It is prepared by soaking the shell in lime juice and calcining in covered crucibles ten to twelve times and finally reducing it to powder.

Action—Anodyne, digestive and astringent.

Uses—As a depilatory a paste made up of conch-shell-ash soaked in the juice of plantain tree and orpiment, in equal parts, is recommended in *Sarngadhara*.

GLYCINE DEBILIS.

SKT.—*Kamboji* [VII. 68].

HINDI—*Bana-urdi, Jangli urad*.

BENG.—*Mashani*.

MAH.—*Rana-udida*.

Habitat—It is found in plains throughout India, Burma and Ceylon.

Parts used—The seed.

Action—Bitter, cooling, astringent and dry.

Uses—The seeds produce semen, strength and blood and cure consumption, fever and disorders of air, bile and blood. Here they are said to form an ingredient of powder for making the mouth fragrant

---

GLYCYRRHIZA GLABRA.

SKT.—*Madhu [Madhvahva,* Lit. 'that which is called *madhu.'* VI. 26], *Yashti* [VI. 29, 62, 66].

ENG.—Sweet wood, liquorice.

HINDI, and PUNJ.—*Mulathi*.

MAH.—*Jashtimadh*.

TAM.—*Ati-madhuram*.

Habitat—Arabia, Persia, Afghanistan and Turkey, but the root is cultivated in the Punjab, Sindh and Peshawar.

Parts used—The peeled root.

Action—Cooling, demulcent, expectorant, diuretic, emmenegogue and gentle laxative.

Uses—It forms an ingredient of several medicines for dysuria, ardor urinae, cough and other bronchial affections. It is also used in aphrodisiacs cheifly because it is a gentle laxative, cooling and demulcent. A mixture containing extracted juice of liquorice root and of *Hermaphrodite Amaranth* taken with honey is said to be a sovereign cure for all sorts of leucorrhœa and other uterine complaints.

GMELINA ARBOREA.

SKT.—*Sriparni* (VI. 95).

HINDI—*Gambhara*.

BENG.—*Gamari*.

MAH.—*Shivanasal*.

TAM.—*Gummadu teku*.

Habitat—The lower Himalayas, the Nilgiris and the East and West coasts of India.

Parts used—The juice of the bark.

Action—Demulcent, stomachic, tonic, refrigerant and laxative.

Uses—With liquorice, sugar and honey it is given as a galactagogue in cases of scanty secretion of milk in women. The application of gingelly oil in which the juice of the bark of *Gmelina Arborea* has been boiled is said to brace up fallen breasts. To prevent abortions in the early stage of pregnancy a powder of the bark, sesame, *Manjishta* and *Satavari* is given in milk.

GRISLEA TOMENTOSA.

SKT.—*Dhataki* (VI. 43).

HINDI—*Dhauta*.

BENG.—*Dhai-phul*.

MAH.—*Pulsathi*.

TAM.—*Dhatari puspam*.

Habitat—Common in many parts of India.

Parts used—The flowers.

Action—Stimulant and astringent.

Uses—Externally the powdered flower is sprinkled over foul ulcers and wounds for diminishing their discharge and promoting granulation. For the same purpose a decoction of the flowers is also used as a lotion. Being astringent it has a contractile effect on the tissues and membranes.

GYMNEMA SYLVESTRE.

SKT.—*Mesha-sringi* (VII. 6).

HINDI and PUNJ.—*Medha-singi*.

BENG.—*Chhota-dudhilata*.

MAH.—*Kavali.*
TAM.—*Shiru kurunja.*

Habitat—A climbing plant common in Central and Southern India and on the Western Ghauts and in the Goa territory.

Parts used—The root, the leaves and the acid principle.

Action—Astringent, stomachic, tonic and refrigerant.

Uses—The root has been long reputed as a remedy for snake-bite. The leaves when chewed deaden the sense of taste of sweet and bitter substances. Here it is mentioned as a constituent of a goetic *Tilaka* mark on the fore-head for infatuating others.

HELIX ASPERA (?).

SKT.—*Nakha* (VII. 53, 61, 62, 65).
ENG.—Mollusc shell.
HINDI—*Nakha, Nakhi.*
BENG.—*Nakhi, Gandha-dravya.*
MAH.—*Nakhala, Bagh-nakha.*

Character—It is a dark, brown shell made of numerous plates, placed one upon the other as in bivalve shells. It is hard, bony and opaque, concave on its under-surface where the mollusc resides. The other surface is convex. On this surface the layers are most distinctly marked.

Uses—The shell is used in the form of a paste, as a perfume and in the preparation of various medicated oils. As a hair cosmetic it is highly recommended.

HIBISCUS ROSA SINENSIS.

SKT.—*Japa* (VI. 52).
ENG.—China Rose or Shoe-flower plant.
HINDI—*Jasund, Gudhal.*
BENG.—*Jaba.*
MAH.—*Jasavanda.*
TAM.—*Shamberattai, shappathuppu.*

Habitat—Very common in flower-gardens of India.

Parts used—The flowers.

Action—Refrigerant, emollient, demulcent, aphrodisiac, and emmenagogue.

Uses—The flowers of this plant, fried in *ghee*, are given in menorrhagia. They, along with the leaves of *Celastrus Paniculatus,* are said to restore menstrual flow in cases of amenorrhœa.

HORDEUM VULGARE.

SKT.—*Yava* (VI. 34).
ENG.—Barley.
HINDI and PUNJ.—*Jau.*
BENG.—*Jaba.*
MAH.—*Bajri.*
TAM.—*Barlhi arisi.*

Habitat—This cereal is largely cultivated in several varieties in each of the provinces of India.

Parts used—The dried, decorticated grain called pearl barley and the seed.

Action—Demulcent, nutritious.

Uses—It is highly nutritious food and a valuable vehicle for other medicines, especially oils.

HYDRARGYRUM.

SKT.—*Sankara-bija* (VI. 5). *Sambhu-bija* (VI. 7, 15; VII. 24).
ENG.—Mercury, quick-silver.
HINDI, PUNJ., BENG., and MAH.—*Para.*
TAM.—*Padrasa.*

Source—Mercury is sometimes met with free in Nature in the form of small, shining silvery globules. But it is mostly found as sulphide or native Cinnabar.

Character—It is a shining, silver-white metal liquid, divisible into spherical globules, mobile, without any odour or taste, slowly volatilising at ordinary temperature; insoluble in water, hydrochloric acid or cold sulphuric acid, but soluble in nitric acid and hot sulphuric acid.

Action—Tonic, alterative and antiseptic.

Uses—Internally mercury is used in innumerable aphrodisiac medicines. It is extremely injurious in its effects if it is not used judiciously, properly and under the instructions of a competent medical man. Its local application to male genitals is indicated here for causing orgasm in the woman.

INDIGOFERA TINCTORIA.

SKT.—*Nili* (VI. 83).

ENG.—True Indigo, Dyer's Indigo.

HINDI, PUNJ., and BENG.—*Nil*.

MAH.—*Nila*.

TAM.—*Nilam*.

Habitat—The small erect shrub is extensively cultivated in India, especially in Bengal, Sindh, Oudh, Madras and Bombay.

Parts used—The plant and the cakes made of oxidised product obtained from the juice.

Action—Stimulant, alterative, antiseptic and astringent.

Uses—The plant yields a valuable dye-stuff called Indigo. Here this stuff is used as an ingredient of a hair-dye.

IPOMOEA DIGITATA.

SKT.—*Vidari* (VI. 21).

HINDI and PUNJ.—*Bidari kand*.

BENG.—*Bhuin-kumra*.

MAH.—*Bhui kohala, Pattana*.

TAM.—*Phalmodika, Nelli-kumbala*.

Habitat—Indigenous to the hotter parts of India.

Parts used—The tuberous root.

Action—Tonic, alterative, aphrodisiac and demulcent.

Uses—In spermatorrhœa the juice of the fresh root is given with cumin and sugar. The powder of the root macerated in its own juice and mixed with honey and *ghee* is recommended for use as an aphrodisiac *(Susruta)*. From the powder of the dried root, previously macerated 14 times in its own juice, an aphrodisiac is made by frying it in butter with equal parts of almonds, quince seeds, cl ves, cardamom, nutmeg, *Satavari, Gokhru*, seeds of *Mucuna Pruriens, Musli*, etc., and making the whole into a conservative

with sugar. This conservative is taken dissolved in milk in doses of $\frac{1}{2}$ tola or more.

JASMINUM GRANDIFLORUM.

SKT.—*Jati* (VI. 5, 33, 47 ; V I. 58, 63, 65).

ENG.—The Spanish Jasmine.

HINDI, PUNJ., BENG. and MAH.—*Chambeli, Chameli*.

TAM.—*Jaji-malle*.

Habitat—Generally met with all over India, especially in the temperate regions, and on the temperate Himalaya.

Parts used—The leaves, the flowers and the juice of the leaves.

Action—The leaves are astringent. From the flowers a perfumed oil or otto is prepared which is greatly esteemed as a cooling agent and as a perfume.

Uses—The leaves are chewn in aphthæ and ulcers in the mouth. Some writers mention the use of flowers applied as a plaster to the loins, genitals and pubes as an aphrodisiac. A poultice of the leaves is also used similarly.

JATROPHA MONTANA.

SKT.—*Danti* (VI. 78).

HINDI—*Hakni, Jamalgota*.

PUNJ.—*Jamalgota*.

MAH.—*Jamalgot*.

TAM.—*Nagadanti*.

Habitat—It is found in tropical Himalaya, Deccan, Bengal, and N. Circars.

Parts used—The seed.

Action—Drastic purgative.

Uses—It enters into the composition of medicines for retained secretions, anasarca, constipation, etc.

LAGENARIA VULGARIS.

SKT.—*Katu-tumbi* (VI. 44).

ENG.—The Bitter Bottle-gourd, a kind of Bitter gourd, Bitter pumpkin.

HINDI—*Karvi ghiya, Karvi lauki*.

BENG.—*Tikta lana, Kodu.*
MAH.—*Ran-bhopla.*
TAM.—*Sorai kay.*

Habitat—This climbing plant is found wild and cultivated nearly all over India.

Parts used—The seed.

Action—The oil from the seeds is cooling.

Uses—For vaginal contraction the seeds of bitter gourd and *Symplocos Racemosa*, both ground down with water, from a useful application.

LEEA HIRTA.

SKT., HINDI and BENG.—*Kakajangha* (VI. 14 ; VII. 14),

Habitat—Found in Sikkim, Himalaya, and East Bengal.

Parts used—The tubers or root and the stem.

Action—Astringent, bitter acrid, mucilaginous, stimulant and alleviative of phlegm and bile.

Uses—Here the powder of the root is used in a medicine to be applied on the navel for the increase of retentive power. This, however, appears to be very doubtful.

LUFFA ECHINATA.

SKT.—*Ghosha* (VI. 4, 9).
HINDI, and PUNJ.—*Ghagar bel, Bindaal.*
BENG.—*Ghoshalata.*
MAH.—*Kukadvel, vapala.*

Habitat—This species is found in N. W. India, Guzerat, Sindh, Bombay and East Bengal.

Parts used—The fruit.

Action—Externally stimulant, antiseptic, internally it is bitter and stomachic in small doses and emetic and drastic purgative in large doses.

Uses—Here the powder of the fruit either alone in honey, or in combination with other medicines is claimed to cause early orgasm in women when applied to the genitalia.

MANDRAGORA OFFICINALIS.

SKT.—*Lakshmana*(VI. 60).
ENG.—Mandrake.
HINDI—*Lakmani, Bhagener.*
TAM.—*Katav-jate.*

Habitat—It grows in N. India, Central Asia and South Europe.

Parts used—The root-bark.

Action—Local anæsthetic. It resembles Belladonna in action, but is weaker. It is sedative and narcotic.

Uses—Like *Datura* it is said to increase sexual excitement in both sexes. Sanskrit writers mention its use for ensuring conception and therefore they call it *Eutrada* 'the giver of a son.'

MANGIFERA INDICA.

SKT.—*Amra* (VI. 81 ; VII. 44, 69).
ENG.—Mango tree.
HINDI and BENG.—*Am.*
PUNJ and MAH.—*Ambu.*
TAM.—*Mamaram.*

Habitat—This tree is indigenous to India and is cultivated in many varieties almost everywhere in the plains.

Parts used—The sprouts, the bark and the leaves.

Action—Diaphoretic, astringent, refrigerant and tonic.

Uses—A decoction of the leaves with a little honey is given in aphonia or loss of voice. The leaves are indicated here as an ingredient of concoctions for making the mouth fragrant. The bark enters into the composition of cosmetics for the body, and the sprouts are used in hair-dyes.

MESUA FERREA.

SKT.—*Naga-kesara* (VI. 57), *Kesara*(VI. 59; VII. 10, 50, 66), *Kinjalka* (VII. 13, 67), *Naga-pushpa* (VII. 47), *Naga-kusuma* (VII. 58).

ENG.—Cobra's Saffron.

HINDI and PUNJ.—*Nag Kesar.*

BENG.— *Nagesar.*

MAH.—*Nagchampe.*

TAM.—*Veillutta champakam, Cheru-
nagapu.*

Habitat—Common on the Eastern Hima-
laya, East Bengal and Assam, Eastern and
Western Ghauts, Burma and the Andamans.
It is cultivated in gardens.

Parts used—The flowers.

Action—Bitter, aromatic and astringent.

Uses—The dried flowers are much used
as a fragrant adjunct to decoctions, oils and
cosmetics. They are mentioned here as an
ingredient of medicines for ensuring impregnation.

MIMOSA PUDICA.

SKT.—*Lajjalu.* (VI. 12, 97; VII. 2)

ENG.—The Sensitive plant, Humble
plant, Touch-me-not.

HINDI and PUNJ.—*Lajvanti.*

BENG.—*Lajak.*

MAH.—*Lajri.*

TAM.—*Thottalpadi, Thottal shurungi.*

Habitat—The sensitive shrub, a native
of Brazil, has long been naturalised and
is plentiful in the hotter regions of India.

Parts used—The root and the leaves.

Action—The root is aphrodisiac, and
the leaves are resolvent and alterative.

Uses—Here the powder of the root along
with other things is used externally on the
soles of the feet for increasing retentive
power. But this is doubtful. The leaves
rubbed into a paste applied to hydrocele,
glandular swellings, and relaxed breasts.

MIMOSA RUBRICAULIS (?).

SKT.—*Sarja-rasa* (VII. 27).

HINDI and PUNJ.—*Ral.*

BENG.—*Shinkanta.*

TAM.—*Sarijarasamu, Chandra.*

Habitat—The tree called *Shorea Robusta*
from which *Mimosa Rubricaulis* is obtained, is
grown on the Western Himalaya and Kumaon.

Parts used—The exudation of the tree

in the form of gum.

Action—The smoke arising from burning
the gum is said to be disinfectant.

Uses—Its is used as an ingredient of
incense.

MORINGA PTERYGOSPERMA.

SKT.—*Sigru* (VII 55).

ENG.—Horse radish, Drum-stick plant.

HINDI and PUNJ.—*Sohanjana.*

BENG.—*Sajna.*

MAH.—*Shegat, Murungamul.*

TAM.—*Murungai.*

Habitat—A beautiful tree wild in the
sub-Himalayan range and commonly cultivated in India and Burma.

Parts used—The bark, root, fruit,
flowers, leaves, seed and gum.

Action—Anti-spasmodic, stimulant, and
diuretic. The gum is bland and mucilaginous.

Uses—The uses of the different. parts
of this tree are manifold. But here probably
the gum is indicated as an ingredient of a
perfume.

MOSCHUS MOSCHIFERUS.

SKT.—*Kasturi* (VII. 58, 63).

ENG.—Musk.

HINDI, PUNJ., BENG. & MAH.—*Kasturi.*

TAM.—*Kasturi.*

Source—Musk-deer, found generally
in China, Russia, Assam, Central Asia, and
pine-forests and the inaccessible cliffs of the
Himalayas above 8,000 feet.

Character—Musk is a dried secretion
from the preputial follicles of the musk-
animal.

Action—Stimulant and aphrodisiac.

Uses—Musk is largely used in perfumery,
its aroma being very lasting and holding
more evanescent perfumes with it. As an
aphrodisiac it is given in combination with
other aphrodisiacs in seminal weakness and
impotence.

MUCUNA PRURIENS (?).

SKT.—*Kapi* (VI. 23).

ENG.—The Cowhage or Cowitch-plant.

HINDI—*Kavach.*

PUNJ.—*Kaunch.*

BENG.—*Alkushi.*

MAH.—*Kuhili.*

TAM.—*Poonaikkali.*

Habitat—An annual climbing shrub common in the tropics and found cultivated in some parts for the sake of its golden-brown velvety legumes, which are cooked and eaten as a vegetable.

Parts used—The seed.

Action—Astringent, nervine tonic and aphrodisiac.

Uses—The seeds are prescribed in the form of powder in doses of 29 to 40 grains spermatorrhœa, Leucorrhœa, etc. A compound powder of these seeds and of the fruits of *Tribulus Terrestris*, taken in equal parts, is recommended to be administered in doses of one drachm with sugar and tepid milk as an aphrodisiac.

MUSA SAPIENTUM.

SKT.—*Rambha* (VI. 50, 51, 92; VII. 37).

ENG.—The Plantain or Banana tree.

HINDI, PUNJ., BENG. and MAH.—*Kela.*

TAM.—*Kadali, Valei.*

Habitat—The plantain tree is cultivated universally in many varieties throughout India.

Parts used—The juice of the plant and of its root.

Action—Astringent and styptic.

Uses—The juice of the plantain tree is used in depilatories and also for curing inflammation, blisters and black spots on the skin.

MYRISTICA FRAGRANS.

SKT.—*Jati-phala* (VII. 37), *Jati-sasyaka* (VII. 66).

ENG.—Nutmeg.

HINDI, PUNJ. and BENG.—*Jaephal.*

MAH.—*Jayiphal.*

TAM.—*Judikay.*

Habitat—The nutmeg tree is indigenous to the Malaya Peninsula and Penang. It has been successfully cultivated in Madras and Southern India.

Parts used—The dried seed and mace.

Action—Nutmeg is stimulant, carminative, and aromatic. Mace is carminative, aphrodisiac and tonic.

Uses—Nutmegs are largely employed as flavouring agent and condiment.

MYRTUS CARYOPHYLLUS.

SKT.—*Lavangaka* (VI. 93).

ENG.—Cloves.

HINDI and PUNJ.—*Laung.*

BENG. and MAH.—*Lavanga.*

TAM.—*Kirambu.*

Habitat—India and Ceylon.

Parts used—The fruit.

Action=Aromatic, antiseptic, local anæsthetic and rubefacient.

Uses—Cloves are mentioned here as ingredient of an unguent for bracing up the breasts.

NARDOSTACHYS JATAMANSI.

SKT.—*Jata* (VII. 6), *Mamsi* (VII. 53, 54, 62).

ENG.—Musk-root, Indian Spike-nard.

HINDI and PUNJ.—*Jatamashi, Bal-chhar.*

MAH.—*Jatamavshi.*

TAM.—*Jatamashi.*

Habitat—This herb grows at great elevations up to 17,000 feet on the Alpine Himalaya, in Nepal, Bhutan, and Sikkim.

Parts used—The rhizome.

Action—Aromatic, tonic, sedative to spinal cord, and nerve stimulant.

Uses—*Jatamamsi* is generally used as an aromatic adjunct in the preparation of medicinal oils and perfumery.

NERIUM ODO UM.

SKT.—*Haya-rɪpu* (VI. 31), *Asvari* (VI. 93), *Hayari* (VI. 94).
ENG.—Sweet-scented Oleander, Rose-berry Spurge.
HɪNDI and PUNJ.—*Kaner*.
BENG.—*Karɑbi*.
MAH.—*Kanera*.
TAM.—*Kanaveeram, Alari*.

Habitat—This small, evergreen shrub is wild in Afghanistan and Northern India, and cultivated in gardens for its flowers.

Parts used—The root and the rootbark.

Action—Poisonous, resolvent and attenuant. Only for external use.

Uses—It is indicated here for bracing up the breasts and toning up the male organ of sex.

OCIMUM MINIMUM.

SKT.—*Maruvaka* (VII. 51).
ENG.—Bush-basil, Marjoram.
HɪNDI and PUNJ.—*Marua*.
Habitat—Found all over India.

Parts used—Leaves.

Action—Demulcent, aromatic.

Uses—The leaves are used for seasoning food and in bathing perfumes.

ORYZA SATIVA.

SKT.—*Tandula* (VI. 27, 53).
ENG.—Rice.
HɪNDI—*Chaval*.
PUNJ. and BENG.—*Chaul*.
MAH.—*Tandul, Bhat*.
TAM.—*Arshi, Nelli* (paddy).

Habitat—This is a principal food crop of India, and is spread over the tropical and sub-tropical regions of both hemispheres.

Parts used—The grain.

Action—Nutrient.

Uses—It is an article of food used all over the world, and as staple food in Bengal, Assam, Burma, Madras, Kashmir and several parts of Bombay Presidency. A special variety of rice of quick growth, ripening in about 60 days *(shashtik-odbhava)* are said to be roborant (VI. 27).

PANDANUS ODORATISSIMUS.

SKT.—*Ketaki* (VII. 51, 68).
ENG.—Fragrant Screw-pine, Caldera bush.
HɪNDI, PUNJ. and BENG.—*Keora*.
MAH.—*Ksvda*.
TAM.—*Talamchedi, Kedagai*.

Habitat—Found wild in Southern India, Burma and the Andamans. Cultivated in gardens.

Parts used—The flowers.

Action—Stimulant, aromatic.

Uses—A fragrant otto and aqua *(Keora-ka-arak)* prepared from flowering tops or bracts in water by distilliation are used medicinally as well as perfumery and for flavouring foods and sweets.

PANICUM DACTYLON.

SKT.—*Durva* (VI. 53).
ENG.—Panic grass, Bent grass, Couch grass.
HɪNDI and BENG.—*Durba*.
PUNJ.—*Khabbal ghas, Dub*.
MAH.—*Haryali, Ọoorva*.
TAM.—*Arugu, Mooyarpul*.

Habitat—The elegant, perennial grass grows everywhere throughout India.

Action—The herb is acid and hæmostatic.

Uses—It is generally given with milk and is useful in dysuria and irritation of the urinary organs. It is claimed here to be emmenagogue in combination with other drugs.

PARMELIA PERLATA [?]

SKT.—*Saileya* (VII. 58), *Silatmaja* (VII. 61).
ENG.—Stone flowers, Yellow lichen, Rockmoss.

HINDI—*Charela, Patthar-ke-phul.*
BENG.—*Sailaja.*
MAH.—*Dagad-phul.*

Habitat—It is found on trees, old planks, walls, and on rocks on the Himalayas, Punjab, Persia, etc.

Action—Bitter, astringent, resolvent, emollient, demulcent.

Uses—The lichen is much used as an incense, especially to releave headache, and also in the preparation of an hair-wash.

PAVONIA ODORATA [?]

SKT.—*Jala* (VII. 25, 56), *Ambhas* (VII. 62), *Ambu* (VII. 47, 55, 57).
HINDI—*Netra-vala, Sugandh-bala.*
BENG.—*Bala.*
MAH.—*Kala-vala, Randodki.*
TAM.—*Peramuttai, Avibattam.*

Habitat—The herb grows wild in U. P., the Western Peninsula, Sindh and Burma.

Parts used—The herb and the root.

Action—Cooling, demulcent, aromatic.

Uses—The herb and the root have a musk-like odour, and are used in perfumes and cosmetics.

PHASEOLUS RADIATUS.

SKT.—*Masha* (VI. 24, 34).
ENG.—Common pulse bean.
HINDI and MAH.—*Urad.*
PUNJ.—*Manh.*
BENG.—*Mash kulay.*
TAM.—*Ulundu.*

Habitat—Cultivated all over India.

Action—It is the most demulcent, cooling as well as nutritious of all pulses, also aphrodisiac and nervine tonic, the only drawback being that it causes wind (flatus).

Uses—It is used in seminal debility, leucorrhœa and other uterine complaints. As a nervine tonic, a confection made of its *dal* is very useful.

PHYSALIS FLEXUOSA.

SKT.—*Vaji-gandha* (VI. 31, 45, 58, 93), *Haya-gandha* (VI. 34).

ENG.—Winter Cherry.
HINDI and PUNJ.—*Asgandh.*
MAH.—*Asagandha.*
TAM.—*Achuvagandhi.*

Habitat—This shurb is common in Bombay and Western India, occasionally met with in Bengal. The root smells like a horse and hence the name.

Parts used—The root and the leaves.

Action—Tonic, alterative, aphrodisiac and nervine sedative.

Uses—The root is used in doses of about 30 grains in cases of general debility, nervous exhaustion, brain-fag, loss of memory, spermatorrhœa, and seminal debility, Externally, in combination with other drugs it is said to be useful in developing the male organ, in contracting the vagina, and in making the breasts turgid.

PINUS DEODARA.

SKT.—*Deva-daru* (VI. 41), *Sura-daru* (VI. 48), *Deva-kashtha* (VI. 53.)
ENG.—Himalayan Cedar.
HINDI—*Deodar, Toona.*
PUNJ.—*Dyar.*
BENG.—*Toon.*
MAH.—*Devataram.*
TAM.—*Toon-maram.*

Habitat—All over the Northern Himalaya; largely cultivated in India.

Parts used—The wood and the bark.

Action—Astringent.

Uses—The powdered bark with other ingredients is here claimed to be an emmenagogue when taken internally while its application to the vagina serves to contract it.

PIPER BETLE.

SKT.—*Naga-valli* [VII 34, 37, 59], *Tambula* [VII, 65, 60].
ENG.—Betel-leaf.
HINDI, PUNJ., BENG. and MAH.—*Pan.*
TAM.—*Vettilœ.*

Habitat—This twining plant is cultivated very extensively in the warm and moist parts of India for its leaves.

Parts used—The leaves.

Action—Stimulant, astringent, aphrodisiac, antiseptic, and aromatic.

Uses—The leaves sweeten the breath, improve the voice and remove fœtor from the mouth.

PIPER LONGUM.

Skt.—*Pippali* (VI. 10, 34; VII. 6), *Kana* (VI. 59, 83, 93; VII. 6).
Eng.—Long pepper, The dried Catkins.
Hindi and Beng.—*Pipli.*
Punj.—*Magh.*
Mah.—*Mothli, Pimpli.*
Tam.—*Tippali.*

Habitat—This plant is indigenous to North-Eastern and Southern India, and Ceylon, and cultivated in Eastern Bengal for its fruit.

Parts used—The immature berries dried in the sun.

Action—Stimulant, alterative, tonic, aphrodisiac, an emmenagogue, externally rubefacient. The root is stimulant.

Uses—The fruit is used to some extent as a spice. The root is much used as a stimulant remedy and also as a spice. Here *Piper Longum* is used along with other drugs as an external application for bracing up the breasts, developing the male organ, etc.

PIPER NIGRUM.

Skt.—*Maricha* (VI. 10, 34). *Ushana* (VI. 59).
Eng.—Black pepper.
Hindi, Punj. and Beng.—*Kali-mirich.*
Mah.—*Kala-miri.*
Tam.—*Milagu.*

Habitat—This perennial climbing shrub is indigenous to Malabar and Travancore coasts.

Parts used—The dried unripe fruit.

Action—Acrid, pungent and hot. Externally it is rubefacient, stimulant to the skin resolvent.

Uses—Its uses are similar to those of *Piper Longum* mentioned above.

PLUMBAGO ZEYLANICA.

Skt.—*Agni-taru.* (VI. 74).
Eng.—Ceylon leadwort, White leadwort.
Hindi, Punj. and Beng.—*Chitra.*
Mah.—*Chitramula.*
Tam.—*Chttira.*

Habitat—This plant grows wild in Bengal, Southern India and Ceylon.

Parts used—The root.

Action—Alterative, gastric stimulant; in large doses it is an acro-narcotic poison. Locally it is vasicant. It has a specific action on the uterus. The scraped root is introduced into the mouth of the womb for the purpose of procuring abortion.

Uses—The decoction of the root will expel the fœtus from the womb whether dead or alive. It is, therefore, employed to procure criminal abortion.

PLUMBI CARBONAS.

Skt.—*Naga-churna* (VI. 49).
Eng.—White lead, Hair powder.
Hindi, Punj. and Beng.—*Sufeda.*
Mah.—*Sapeta.*
Tam.—*Velliya.*

Source—It is found in Nature, both as crystallised and in a massive state. The soft, heavy, white powder is artificially prepared by suspending sheets of lead over the vapours of heated vinegar. The corroded rust when collected is known as *Sufeda.*

Action—It is used locally as a sedative and as an astringent.

Uses—It is used in depilatories.

PLUMBI OXIDUM RUBRUM.

Skt.—*Sindura* (VI. 6; VII. 22).
Eng.—Red lead, minium.
Hindi, Punj., Beng. & Mah.—*Sendhur.*
Tam.—*Sagappusinduram.*

Source—It is obtained by heating oxide

of lead to very high temperature.

Action—It is a local stimulant and is used in ointments liniments.

Uses—When applied with other things to the male organ before coitus, it is claimed to cause an early orgasm in women.

PONGAMIA GLABRA.

Skt.—*Karanja* (VI. 19; VII. 46), *Karanjaka* (VII. 62).
Eng.—Indian Beech.
Hindi—*Korang, Kidamal.*
Punj.—*Suckchain.*
Beng.—*Dahar Karanja.*
Mah.—*Kidamar.*
Tam.—*Pungam-maram.*

Habitat—This tree is common all over India.

Parts used—The seed.

Action—Bitter, acrid, stimulant astringent and anti-parasitic.

Uses—The expressed oil from the seeds has antiseptic and stimulant, healing properties. It is applied to skin diseases, in scabies, sores, herpes, etc. Taken internally, the seeds are stimulant. They are also used in perfumes.

PRUNUS MAHALEB (?)

Skt.—*Phalini* (VII 13).

A medicinal plant and perfume (described in some places as a fragrant seed). It is also known as *Priyangu* in Sanskrit.

PTEROCARPUS SANTALINUS.

Skt.—*Kalanga* (VII. 25).
Eng.—Red Sandalwood.
Hindi—*Lal chandan.*
Beng. and Mah.—*Rakta-chandana.*
Tam.—*Shen-chandanam.*

Habitat—This small tree is generally met with in the forests of Southern India.

Parts used—The wood.

Action—Mildly astringent and tonic.

Uses—The hard wood of red sandal is called *Santalum Rubrum* and enters into the composition of numerous astringent remedies and of incense.

PUNICA GRANATUM.

Skt.—*Dadima* (VI. 48; VII. 49), *Dadimi* (VI 96, VII. 45).
Eng.—Pomegranate.
Hindi and Punj.—*Anar.*
Beng.—*Darim.*
Mah.—*Dalimba.*
Tam.—*Madalai.*

Habitat—This tree is cultivated nearly all over India.

Parts used—The rind of the fruit.

Action—The rind of the fruit is astringent and stomachic.

Uses—Being an astringent, it has contractile action on the tissues and the skin, when applied locally.

QUERCUS INFECTORIA.

Skt.—*Maju-phala* (VI 83).
Eng.—Oak galls, Magic nuts, Gall nuts.
Hindi, Punj., Beng. and Mah.—*Maju-phala.*
Tam.—*Machakai.*

Habitat—The tree is a native of Greece and Asia Minor extending to Persia. The galls are imported into India.

Parts used—The nut.

Action—Astringent.

Uses—It is mentioned here as an ingredient of a hair-dye.

RHUS SUCCEDANA.

Skt.—*Sringi* (VII. 27).
Eng.—The Galls.
Hindi, Punj., Beng. & Mah.—*Kakrasingi.*
Tam.—*Kakkata Shingi.*

Habitat—Himalayan mountain ranges on the North-West from Kashmir to Simla.

Parts used—The galls.

Uses—It is used as an ingredient of incense.

RUBIA MUNJISTA.

SKT.—*Sona-yashti* (VI 92), *Manjishta* (VII. 4).
ENG.—The Indian Madder.
HINDI and PUNJ.—*Majith.*
BENG.—*Manjit.*
MAH.—*Manjista, Chitra-valli.*
TAM.—*Manditta.*

Habitat—It is a climbing plant growing in the North-West Himalaya, Nilgiris and other hilly districts of India.

Parts used—The root.

Uses—A paste made by rubbing up the roots with honey is a valuable application for freckles and other discolorations of the skin.

SALVADORA PERSICA.

SKT —*Pilu-taru* (VII. 48).
ENG.— The Tooth-brush tree
HINDI, PUNJ. and BENG.—*Chhota Pilu.*
TAM.—*Ughaiputtai.*

Habitat—This tree is found in the Punjab and North-Western India and Persia.

Parts used—The flowers.

Action—Stimulant, laxative, and aromatic.

Uses—The dried flowers, powdered and formed with other aromatic substances into an unguent, serve as a cosmetic for the body and remove offensive smell thereof.

SANTALUM ALBUM.

SKT.—*Chandana.* (VII. 24, 25, 27, 44, 47, 55, 57, 58).
HINDI and PUNJ.—*Chandan.*
BENG.—*Swet-chandan.*
MAH.—*Safed chandan.*
TAM.—*Chandan kattai.*

Habitat—This small ever-green tree is indigenous to Mysore, grown also in Coimbatore and the Southern part of Madras.

Parts used—The wood.

Action—Bitter cooling, sedative and astringent.

Uses—This fragrant wood has been used in India in Hindu religious and social ceremonials from very early times. Applied externally in the form of a paste, it allays heat and pruritus. An emulsion of the wood is used as a cooling application to the skin, in erysipelas, prurigo and Sudamina. It is one of the main constituents of several cosmetic preparations and incense.

SAPINDAS DETERGENS.

SKT.—*Arishta* (VI. 48).
ENG.—Indian Filbert, Soap-nut tree.
HINDI, PUNJ. and MAH.—*Ritha, rethra.*
BENG.—*Bara-Ritha.*
TAM.—*Ponan-kottai, Puvandi.*

Habitat—Several species of the genus *Sapindaceæ* are quite common in Southern India and cultivated in Bengal.

Parts used—The fruit and the seed.

Uses—The fruits are largely used as soap-substitute for washing both cloth and hair. Pessaries made of the kernel of the seeds are used to stimulate the uterus to child birth and in amenorrhœa.

SARACA INDICA.

SKT.—*Asoka* (VI 51).
ENG.—The Asoka tree.
HINDI, and MAH.—*Ashoka.*
BENG.—*Anganapriya.*
TAM.—*Asogam.*

Habitat—It is grown in the gardens throughout India.

Parts used—The flowers.

Uses—The flowers are used in bathing perfumes.

SAUSSUREA AURICULATA.

SKT.—*Kushtha* (VI. 31, 33, 34, 93 : VII. 11, 14, 67, 68), *Kushthaka* (VI. 45; VII 4), *Vyadhi* (VII. 25, 60), *Arti* (VII 44).

ENG.—The Costus.
HINDI and PUNJ.—*Kuth*.
BENG.—*Pachak*.
TAM.—*Gostan*.

Habitat—Growing abundantly on the mountains around Kashmir.

Parts used—The root.

Action—Antiseptic, disinfectant, expectorant, aromatic stimulant, acrid, tonic, alterative and aphrodisiac.

Uses—Externally the powder of the root is used as an ointment and applied to ulcers and other skin diseases, and also for resolving tumours. The root is chiefly used as a perfume and its dried powder is a useful hair wash. It also forms an ingredient of aphrodisiac medicines.

SCINDAPSUS OFFICINALIS.

SKT.—*Dvirada-pippali* (VI. 31).
HINDI—*Bari pipli*.
BENG.—*Gaj-pipul*.
MAH.—*Thora-pimpli*.
TAM.—*Atti-tippaili*.

Habitat—It is a large climbing plant growing in tropical parts of India.

Parts used—The fruit.

Action—Stimulant and aromatic.

Uses—Its external application is said to promote the development of the *membrum virile*.

SEMECARPUS ANACARDIUM.

SKT.—*Bhallata* (VI. 36), *Raksho bhuruha* (VI 76.)
ENG.—The Marking-nut tree.
HINDI and BENG.—*Bhela, Bhilawa*.
PUNJ.—*Bhalanvan*.
MAH.—*Bibba*.
TAM.—*Shenkottai*.

Habitat—The tree is found growing on mountainous parts of the tropical India.

Parts used—The fruit or nut.

Action—Stimulant and a escharotic.

Uses—The bruised nut is applied to the *os uteri* by women to procure abortion. Internally taken, it is said to act as a contraceptive. But great caution must be taken when using it internally, in fact not without competent medical advice. Being caustic in action, it is applied to the male organ for developing it by promoting circulation of the blood.

SESAMUM INDICUM.

SKT.—*Tila* (VI 48, 77, 85).
HINDI, PUNJ. and BENG.—*Til*.
MAH.—*Teel*.
TAM.—*Ellu*.

Habitat—This small bush is indigenous to India extensively cultivated in the warmer regions. The black quality is most common yields the best quality of oil and is also the best suited for medicinal purposes.

Parts used—The seed and the flowers.

Action—Demulcent and emollient.

Uses—Sesame is largely used in sweets in India. The oil extracted from the seeds is an article of daily use in every Indian household. Its uses are too numerous to be mentioned. Here the seeds are indicated in a preparation intended to make the vagina redolent. The seeds and the flowers are also mentioned as hair-promoters, etc.

SIDA CORDIFOLIA.

SKT.—*Bala* (VI. 23, 31, 62, 97).
ENG.—Country Mallow (seeds).
HINDI and PUNJ.—*Khareti*.
BENG.—*Barela*.
MAH.—*Chikana, Tupkaria*.
TAM —*Mayir-manikham, Paniyar tutti*.

Habitat—It is common all over India.

Parts used—The root.

Action—The root is astringent, aphrodisiac and tonic.

Uses—The root is used in *Brihat-Asvagandha Ghrita* and other preparations for increasing sexual power. Externally applied, it is claimed here to brace up the breasts and to develop the male organ. Internally used it is also averred to ensure impregnation.

SIDA SPINOSA.

SKT.—*Naga-bala* (VI. 23, 31), *Matanga-bala* (VI 38).
HINDI—*Gulsakri.*
BENG.—*Gorak chaulia.*
MAH.—*Tukati-khareti.*

Habitat—It is another species of *Sida (Bala)*, found throughout the hotter parts of India and Ceylon.

Parts used—The root.

Action—Astringent, aphrodisiac and tonic.

Uses—It is indicated here for bringing about an early orgasm in woman and also for developing the male organ.

SILICATE OF ALUMINA AND OXIDE OF IRON.

SKT.—*Gairika* (VI. 92).
ENG.—Red Ochre, Red earth, Bole Rubra.
HINDI and PUNJ.—*Geru, Geri.*
MAH.—*Geru.*
TAM.—*Sona-geru.*

Source—It is a clay found in lead and iron ore and contains more of oxide of iron than any other clay.

Action—Sweetish, astringent and cooling.

Uses—It is useful as a local application for burns, ulcers, boils, pustular eruptions and aphthous sores about the mouth.

SINAPIS GLAUCA.

SKT.—*Gaura-sarshapa* (VI. 34).
ENG.—White mustard.
HINDI and PUNJ.—*Gori-sarson.*
BENG.—*Saris.*

Habitat—It is extensively cultivated throughout tropical India.
Parts used—The seed.
Action—Rubefacient.

Uses—It is largely used in skin diseases. Being a rubefacient, it promotes circulation of blood and is therefore recommended in a local application for developing the male organ.

SODA CARBONAS IMPURA.

SKT.—*Sarji* (VI. 58).
ENG.—*Dhobi's* earth, Barilla, Natron.
HINDI and MAH.—*Sajji-Khar.*
PUNJ.—*Sajji.*
TAM.—*Choontoomunnoo, Sanchhi karam.*

Source—Obtained from the ashes of Chenopodiaceous plants, a species of salt worts growing near the sea. Also from kelp or barilla by incinerating sea weeds, from *Dhobi's* earth by adding quick-lime to the earth and boiling repeatedly with water. It occurs in porous, granular masses, of a greyish white colour or as heavy hard pieces, with a strong alkaline taste of soda.

Action—It is antacid, alterative, and diuretic.

Uses—A weak solution of it is injected into the vagina to check leucorrhœa. It is an efficient remedy in urinary diseases such as uric acid gravel and suppression of urine. In amenorrhœa a paste made in milk, of equal parts of *sajji* and Heart pea, sweet-flag and *Asana* is useful.

SODII BIBORAS.

SKT.—*Tankana* (VI. 7, 8, 33).
ENG.—Borax, Biborate of Sodium.
HINDI, PUNJ. and BENG.—*Sohaga.*
MAH.—*Kankankhar.*
TAM.—*Venharam.*

Source—It occurs in Nature. Crude borax is found in masses by evaporation of water, on shores of lakes in Tibet and also in crystals. It is also obtained from the mud of lakes surrounded by hills in Nepal.

Action—Astringent, antacid, and local sedative and antiseptic.

Uses—It is claimed here as being useful for causing early orgasm in woman and for developing the male organ.

SODIUM CHLORIDE IMPURA.

SKT.—*Saindhava* (VI. 34, 83, 90).
ENG.—Rock salt, Bay salt.
HINDI and PUNJ.—*Sendha lon.*
MAH.—*Sendhur-lavana.*

TAM.—*Indu-uppu.*

Source—It is found in nature in extensive beds, mostly associated with clay and calcium sulphate.

Character—It is found in small, white crystalline grains or transparent cubes. It is brownish white externally and white internally.

Uses—It is recommended here in preparations for developing the male organ, for promoting the growth of hair and for acne.

SOLANUM INDICUM.

SKT.—*Brihati* (VI. 34, 36).
ENG.—The Indian night shade.
HINDI—*Barhanta.*
PUNJ.—*Kandyari.*
BENG.—*Byakura.*
MAH.—*Dolimoola.*
TAM.—*Kari-mulli.*

Habitat—This plant is common all over India.

Parts used—The fruit.

Action—Astringent, aphrodisiac and re solvent.

Uses—It is seldom used alone. As a local application, it is given here as an ingredient of a *recipe* for developing the male organ.

SO NUM JACQUINII.

SKT.—*Kshudra* (VI. 59).
ENG.—Wild Egg plant, Bitter-sweet Woody Night-shade.
HINDI—*Kateli.*
PUNJ.—*Chhoti Kandyari.*
BENG.—*Kantakari.*
MAH.—*Bhuiringani.*
TAM.—*Kandankattari.*

Habitat—This plant is common everywhere, especially on the east and west coasts of India.

Parts used—The fruit and the root.

Uses—It is used in dysuria, costiveness, fevers and low vitality of the general system.

SOLANUM NIGRUM.

SKT.—*Kakamachi* (VI. 85).
HINDI and PUNJ.—*Mako.*
BENG.—*Kakamachai.*
TAM.—*Manattakkali.*

Habitat—This herb is common throughout India.

Parts used—The entire herb.

Action—Alterative sedative, diaphoretic; locally anodyne.

Uses—In the form of a poultice the herb is used in skin diseases. But here it is mentioned as an ingredient of a hair-dye.

SYMPLOCOS RACEMOSA.

SKT.—*Lodhra* (VI. 10, 38, 44, 90; VII. 44, 45, 49, 50, 56), *Savara* (VI. 43, 66, 78, 88).
ENG.—The Lodh tree.
HINDI and PUNJ.—*Lodh, Pathani Lodh.*
BENG. and MAH.—*Lodhra.*
TAM.—*Ludduga-chettu.*

Habitat—This is a small tree found in the lower hills of Bengal, Assam and Burma.

Parts used—The bark.

Action—Cooling and mild astringent.

Uses—Its uses are various and manifold. Here it is indicated as forming an ingredient of preparations for causing an early orgasm in woman, contracting the vagina, stabilising the fœtus, developing the male organ, promoting the growth of hair, removing acne, and of cosmetics and perfumes.

TABERNAEMONTANA CORONARIA.

SKT.—*Tagara* (VII. 6, 11, 14, 40).
ENG.—East-Indian Rose-bay, Wax-flower plant, Ceylon Jasmine.
HINDI—*Chandni, Tagar.*
BENG.—*Tagar.*
TAM.—*Nandiyavertam, Gandhi-tagarappu.*

Habitat—It is met with in Bengal and South India.

Parts used—The root.

Action—The root is local anodyne.

Uses—Here it is used for the purpose of black magic.

TAMARINDUS INDICA.

SKT.—*Chincha* (VI. 6 ; VII. 46), *Chin-chinika* (VI. 9).
ENG.—The Tamarind tree.
HINDI and PUNJ.—*Imli.*
BENG.—*Tentul.*
MAH.—*Chinch.*
TAM.—*Puliyam-palam.*

Habitat—It is an evergreen tree, indigenous to South India and cultivated throughout India and Burma.
Parts used—The seed.
Action—Astringent and tonic.
Uses—The seeds are mentioned here as entering into the composition of medicinal preparations for causing an early orgasm in woman, and of cosmetics.

TAXUS BACCATTA (?)

SKT.—*Sthaueya* (VII. 56, 58, 60, 66), *Sthauneyaka* (VII. 63).
ENG.—Himalayan Yew.
HINDI—*Thuner, Thuneer.*
BENG.—*Sugandh.*

Habitat—It is 'a native of temperate Himalayan, Afghanistan to Bhutan and Kassia Hills.

Parts used—The leaves.

Uses—They are used in perfumes and cosmetics.

TERMINALIA ARJUNA.

SKT.—*Pandava-taru* (VI. 81).
ENG.—The Arjun Myrobalan.
HINDI and BENG.—*Arjun, Kahu.*
MAH.—*Shardul, sanmadat.*
TAM.—*Vella-marda.*

Habitat—This tree is found in lower Himalayas, Bengal, Burma, Central and Southern India and Ceylon.

Parts used—The bark.

Action—Astringent and tonic.

Uses—It is mentioned here as a constituent of a hair-dye.

TERMINALIA BELLERICA.

SKT.—A constituent of *Triphala* (VI. 29, 43, 81) called *Vibhitaka.*
ENG.—Belleric myrobalan.
HINDI, PUNJ. and BENG.—*Bahera.*
TAM.—*Taurik kay.*

Habitat—It is common in Indian forests and plains.

Parts used—The fruit.

Action—Astringent and laxative.

Uses—The fruit is a constituent of *Triphala,* a remedy prescribed in a large variety of diseases. *Jogis* consider that kernel of one fruit eaten daily increases the appetite for sexual indulgence. Oil expressed from the kernel is used as a dressing for the hair.

Here, the belleric myrobalan, as an ingredient of *Triphala* is prescribed for contracting the vagina and for preparing a hair-dye. It is also mentioned as an ingredient of an aphrodisiac and roborant preparation.

TERMINALIV CHEBULA.

SKT.—*Pathya* (VI. 54 ; VII. 44, 45, 54, 55, 60, 62), *Haritaki* (VII. 46), *Abhaya* (VII. 62).
ENG.—Chebulic myrobalan, Ink-nut.
HINDI, and PUNJ.—*Pili Harar.*
BENG.—*Hora.*
MAH.—*Hirad.*
TAM.—*Kaduk-kai.*

Habitat—This tree is wild in the forests of Northern India, the Central provinces and Bengal, common in Madras, Mysore and in the Southern parts of the Bombay Presidency.

Parts used—The fruit.

Action—Safe and effective purgative, astringent, alterative and tonic.

Uses—This fruit also forms an ingredient of *Triphala* and is used likewise as the belleric myrobalan. Here the fruit is mentioned in connection with a medicine for menorrhagia and cosmetics and perfumes.

TREWIA NUDIFLORA.

SKT.—*Pindaraka* (VI. 81).
HINDI—*Pindara.*
BENG.—*Pittori.*
PUNJ.—*Main-phal.*

Habitat—The tree is found in various parts of India.

Parts used—The root.

Uses—Like *Terminalia Arjuna,* it is used in a hair-dye.

TRIBULUS LENUGINOSUS.

SKT.—*Gokshura* (VI. 23, 77).
ENG.—Small Caltrops.
HINDI and BENG.—*Gokhru.*
PUNJ.—*Bhakhra.*
MAH.—*Lahan Gokhru.*
TAM.—*Cherunerinche.*

Habitat—This trailing plant is common in sandy soil throughout India, plentiful in the United Provinces and in Madras.

Parts used—The fruit and the root.

Action—Cooling, demulcent, diuretic, tonic and aphrodisiac.

Uses—The plant and the dried spiny fruits are used in decoction or infusion in cases of spermatorrhœa, phosphaturia, diseases of the genito-urinary system, impotence, and seminal debility. The fruits, along with sesame flowers, pounded in cow's milk are claimed to be effective in promoting the growth of hair.

TRISULPHURET OF ARSENIC.

SKT.—*Tala* (VI. 50), *Haritala* (VI. 51).
ENG.—Trisulphuret of Arsenic, Orpiment, Yellow Sulphuret of arsenic.
HINDI and PUNJ.—*Hartal.*
BENG. and MAH.—*Haritala.*
TAM.—*Arridaram.*

Source—Orpiment is found native in China and Persia. It occurs in two forms, viz., in smooth shining, gold-coloured scales and in yellow opaque masses. The former is preferred for internal use.

Uses—As a depilatory orpiment forms an ingredient of several formulæ for the removal of hair, *e. g.,* a paste made up of conch-shell-lime (soaked in the juice of plantain tree) and orpiment in equal parts.

ZINGIBER OFFICINALIS.

SKT.—*Sringavera* (VI. 59).
ENG.—Ginger.
HINDI and PUNJ.—*Adrak.*
BENG.—*Adrakh.*
MAH.—*Alen.*
TAM.—*Shukhu.*

Habitat—Ginger is cultivated in many parts of India; on a large scale in the warm moist regions, chiefly in Madras, Cochin and Travancore and to a somewhat less extent in Bengal and the Punjab.

Parts used—The scraped and dried rhizomes as well as fresh ones.

Action—Aromatic, stimulant, carminative, stomachic, sialagogue and digestive.

Uses—Here the powder of the dried rhizomes is incorporated in a medicine said to be useful in sterility. *Bhava-prakasha* recommends a confection named *Subhagya Sunthi* for disorders of the alimentary canal in females after confinement.

ZIZYPHUS JUJUBA.

SKT.—*Kola* (VI. 94; (VII. 47, 66).
ENG.—Jujube fruit.
HINDI and PUNJ.—*Ber.*
BENG.—*Kula.*
MAH.—*Bor.*
TAM.—*Elandai.*

Habitat—This tree is found wild and cultivated in many parts of India and Burma.

Parts used—The kernel of the seed.

Uses—The kernel of the seed *(Kola-majja)* is said to be entering into the composition of an unguent for bracing up the fallen breasts of women and of cosmetics and an aromatic masticatory.

FINIS